THE SKY
AND ITS MYSTERIES

M 51, Canes Venatici

N.G.C. 4565, Coma Berenices

Two extra-galactic nebulae. Photographed with the 200 inch Hale telescope on Mount Palomar

THE SKY

AND

ITS MYSTERIES

by

ERNEST AGAR BEET
B.Sc., F.R.A.S.

19477

LONDON
G. BELL AND SONS LTD
1962

First published 1952
Reprinted 1957, 1960, 1962

Printed in Great Britain by
Lowe and Brydone (Printers) Limited, London, N.W.10

Preface

THERE are already a very large number of books on general astronomy for the non-specialist, and the only excuse for adding yet another is that I was asked to write it. There was a time when a reasonably comprehensive treatment could be written in one book; those days are now long past. The aim in the present volume is to give an outline of the whole field, so that the newcomer to this science may see clearly how it arose, what it is all about and where unfinished problems lie, and also to give some guidance to further reading in the sections that he may afterwards choose as his own. To this end there are more references than is usual in a book of this kind; it is realised that some of them are not universally available, but they are included for the benefit of students and others who have advantageous library facilities.

An obvious criticism of the book is that the reader is kept too long too near home. That is inevitable in a book with this title; so many of the common mysteries are near home, and it is a secondary aim to explain the impacts of astronomy on our daily life.

The map at the end of the book is drawn solely as an aid to the reader, and convenience when handling the book has been a primary consideration. Some familiar objects will not be found there, for they are not mentioned in the text; it is to supplement, not replace, the normal kind of star map for outdoor use.

My thanks are due to the following for material for the Plates as recorded thereon: the Astronomer Royal (VIII and IX top); Sir Howard Grubb, Parsons & Co.;

5

Messrs. Cox, Hargreaves and Thomson; Professor A. C. B. Lovell, Mr. L. F. Ball; Mr. F. J. Hargreaves; The British Astronomical Association; Mr. T. H. Whittome; Professor L. d'Azambuja (Meudon Observatory); Editor of *Discovery*; also for information regarding Fig. 39 to the Astronomer Royal; for drawing Fig. 4 to Mr. A. R. Steele; to Mr. H. W. Newton for special information regarding the section on the Sun; and to Mr. M. W. Ovenden for material included in Chapter III and for reading and criticising the whole manuscript.

For permission to reproduce copyright material my acknowledgments are due to the Astronomer Royal (Greenwich and Cape photographs), the Directors of the Mount Wilson and Palomar, the Yerkes, the Lick and Norman Lockyer Observatories and to Mr J. Evershed, F.R.S., as noted on the Plates.

E. A. B.

Nautical College,
Pangbourne.

Contents

List of Plates

List of Figures

CHAPTER I

The Mysteries Presented

THE Sky and its Mysteries; this title might be mis-understood, for the great dome of heaven covering our countryside may be considered from different points of view. If you are an artist, who loves the beauty of the clouds and the sunset, or a sportsman wondering whether to bat if you win the toss, or a student of weather for its own sake, then this is the wrong book. These phenomena are products of our own atmosphere and have already been adequately treated in this series (1); in this book we shall study those things which lie far, far beyond our own local environment. The daylight sky is rather taken for granted by most people, and until the late war the night sky was hardly noticed at all. Then, when the man-made lights were put out, many town dwellers felt for the first time the charm and mystery of a sparkling night. This book is not intended to be a practical handbook, for numerous such books already exist, but it is hoped that the reader will take the trouble to go outside and see for himself the substance of this first chapter.

We will begin with the daylight; how much have you noticed about the sun? It moves across the sky from east to west and is highest above the horizon at noon by the sundial, though not necessarily by the clock. Its path across the sky changes throughout the year. At the spring equinox the rising and setting points are east and west, but over the next three months both points move towards the north and the sun at noon becomes steadily higher in the sky. By September the original path has been re-covered and then follows the reverse situation, rising and setting points becoming south of east and west and a low sun at noon. If we travel north or south over the earth's surface, changes will be noticed. For a northern journey in the summer months, for instance, the rising and setting points will move steadily towards the north until they meet and the sun remains visible throughout the 24 hours. At the same time during the journey the midday altitude becomes steadily less. If this book reaches readers south of the equator this paragraph will not quite agree with what they can observe, and they must adapt it to make it fit. Now all this is no mystery to us—it is in the geo-graphy books—but it was a great mystery facing man when he first began to think, and in spite of the geography books it is surprising how many people do not clearly understand it now. Sometimes when a low sun in foggy weather can be studied without our being dazzled, dark spots can be seen on the surface of our luminary, and those supplied another puzzle for our ancestors.

Now consider the observed facts about the moon, be-ginning from what is popularly called 'new moon'. Here we see a thin crescent in the west in the evening and convex towards the setting sun. Sometimes the crescent appears to contain a dim coppery disk, the 'old moon in the young moon's arms'. As the days go by the moon is more and more to the east at sunset, and each day the illuminated strip gets wider until the crescent becomes half a disk, and the half disk a whole one, the 'full moon'. During this part of the month the moon could have been seen during the afternoon if the sky were blue and the observer had looked in the right place, for the moon rises and sets like the sun, but its times of rising and setting become later each day. For the second part of the month the shapes, or phases, are repeated in reverse order, and with the fully illuminated side facing east towards the rising sun. These phases can also be seen in daylight, in the forenoon this time. The daily change in the time of moonrise is roughly 50 minutes, but is not always the same, and can be a few minutes only. This occurs at the autumn full moon, and as the moon then rises at about sunset and does so for several days on end, workers in the fields can carry on with their tasks at a critical time, the time of the 'harvest moon'. The disk of the moon looks always the same, with the same light and dark patches, and at each full moon we see the same 'man in the moon', or whatever figure we learnt in childhood. Is there really a man in the moon? Or will there be some soon? The first question is an old speculation and the second a new ambition.

There are two further phenomena connected with the moon, the first occurring at the time of full moon, when the sun and moon are on opposite sides of the earth. A curved shadow begins to creep over the face of our satellite and the moonlight begins to fade. It may be that in about an hour and a half the moon is completely enveloped and shines very dimly, with a dull coppery light. After, perhaps, half an hour of this darkness, the shadow begins to move away. This phenomenon is a total lunar eclipse, and a diagram showing how it comes about will be found in almost any good atlas. Sometimes the eclipse is only partial and the moon's disk is at no stage fully obscured. Many readers will also have watched, through a smoked glass, a partial eclipse of the sun. We have already noted that the last we see of the old moon is the waning crescent, visible in the morning and convex to the sunrise; we next see the moon a few days later in the evening, convex to the sunset. It sometimes happens that during the intervening period a round object creeps over the surface of the sun so that the bright disk has a piece bitten out. Usually the eclipse is seen to be only partial and the sun is never quite blotted out, but on many such occasions observers in the right part of the world see the eclipse as a total one, a glorious sight, to which reference will be made later. Eclipses of one kind or the other are fairly frequent, but a total solar eclipse is a very rare event in any one locality. The atlas diagrams show why eclipses happen, but they do not explain why these events do not happen every month.

Now let us consider a clear night with no moon, and no artificial lights about. In the first place the observer must allow his eyes to adapt themselves to the darkness, and then he will be able to enjoy to the full the glorious spectacle above. The sky is studded with diamonds; some bright and some faint; some what might be called electric blue, others distinctly orange; some areas with only a few scattered stars and others densely packed; and over all the silvery band, from horizon to horizon, the Milky Way. There is mystery here, and the questions of what are the stars, why do they shine, and what is their distance from us, at once present themselves. In later chapters some effort will be made to explain these things and to show how the astronomer finds out so much about them. He is at a disadvantage compared with other scientists, for he can neither touch his material nor exercise any control over it—he can only watch it from afar and draw inferences from what he sees. For the moment, however, what can the reader see for himself?

At first the large number of stars is rather confusing, for

about 3,000 individual stars are visible to the unaided eye on a good night. They have, however, from very ancient times, been divided into groups called constellations, and once a few of these have been learnt and can be readily recognised, wherever they lie, the study of the sky becomes so much easier. Very few will be described here and the reader should supplement this book with some simple star guide (2). The most familiar grouping for observers north of the equator is the Plough (Fig. 1), a group of seven stars forming a part of the ancient constellation of the Great Bear. The astronomer uses the Latin Ursa Major, and in America the

Fig. 1.   The Plough and the Pole Star

seven are usually known as the Big Dipper. Most of these seven stars are of the second magnitude; the 20 or so brighter ones are of the first magnitude, and third, fourth and fifth lead down to the faintest that we ordinarily see. When you look for this group it may not be the same way around as in the drawing, and if you look at it at hourly intervals for a long winter evening, you will find that it is moving all the time. Careful observation will show that it is moving in a circle about the star marked P, which is named Polaris or the Pole Star. Note that the stars α and β (Alpha and Beta) called the Pointers, point approximately towards it, and P is at a distance of rather over four times that from α to β. The

popular landmark for observers south of the equator is
the Southern Cross, Fig. 2. α and β are of the first
magnitude, while γ and α guide the observer to the centre
of rotation X; unfortunately in this case there is no star
to mark the spot. The point X is called the south celestial
pole; the north celestial pole is very close to P in Fig. 1.

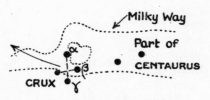

Fig. 2. The Southern Cross

The Plough and the Southern Cross (astronomers'
name: Crux) are quite near to their respective poles;
Fig. 3 shows three constellations that are further from the
poles, Orion being just midway between the two. These
three have been chosen as being prominent and easy to
remember. Orion, named after a mythological hero, is
well seen in the southern half of the evening sky from
December to March, the Lion (Leo) from February to
June, and the Swan (Cygnus) from June to December.
Observers in the southern hemisphere will be able to see
Orion and the Lion, and possibly the Swan, but they will
be upside down and in the northern half of the sky. If you
watch one of these for an evening you can see it moving

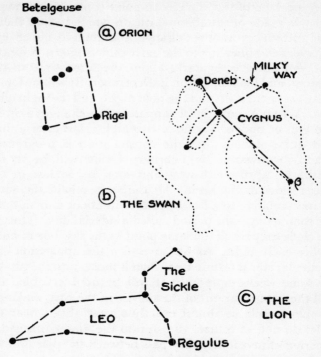

Fig. 3. Three prominent constellations

from east to west like the sun and moon. The two sets of observations show that the whole of the heavens, north and south, seem to rotate about the earth once a day, the two poles marking the axis of rotation. Stars near the poles move in small circles the whole of which we see; they are said to be circumpolar. Stars further away have larger circles which carry them below the horizon so that they rise and set.

B

In speaking of the non circumpolar constellations mention was made of suitable months in which to find them. This introduces another change apparent to naked eye observers and puzzling to the early philosophers. Suppose that you observe regularly about the same time in the evening, and look for Orion in December. It will be found well over to the east, and the next night, and the night after that. Without some simple apparatus no change in direction will be noticed in one or two nights, but after a time it is quite obvious that the constellation is progressing steadily westward. By February Orion will be to the south; in April south-west and soon to be lost in the sunset glow in the west. All the stars regain the same position relative to a fixed observer in about four minutes less than a day—the period called a siderial day. Thus by the clock they reach the same point in the sky four minutes earlier each night. As we have seen the apparition of a particular star is terminated when it passes into the sunset; for some weeks or months it will be unobservable, and will then reappear out of the sunrise in the east, making a complete cycle in almost exactly a year. Stars near the poles do not, of course, vanish into the sunset; instead of a period of invisibility they pass between the pole and the horizon directly below it.

When the night is really clear and dark the Milky Way, also known as the Galaxy (from the Greek word for milk) is a joy to behold. This silvery band, shown by telescopes to consist of myriads of faint stars, completely encircles the earth, though of course one cannot see it all at once and the most southerly part of it is never seen from England. For a part of its length it forms a double stream, in fact the division begins in our selected constellation of Cygnus. Crux also lies in the Milky Way, in the part not visible from England, and here there is a curious dark patch called the Coal Sack. The Milky Way raises a number of questions. Does it really represent a ring of stars around our world? Are the stars faint, or very distant, or both? Is the Coal Sack a hole or an obstruction? Why is there a rift in Cygnus? Unravelling the apparent motion of the heavens is now a matter of history (Ch. II); the mystery of the Milky Way is a modern problem the writer will attempt to explain in Ch. VII.

The stars hitherto considered are known as the 'fixed stars', because the patterns by which we remember them remain constant for generations. Anyone studying them will sooner or later find an object that does not belong to the pattern. It may be a Nova, or temporary star, which shines out for a few days and then gradually fades away. A planet or 'wandering star' is much more probable and there are five of these visible to the naked eye, though one of them, Mercury, is unlikely to be found by accident. Venus at its best is a brilliant and beautiful object in the western sky in the evening or in the eastern sky in the morning; it is not visible in the middle of the night, but it is sometimes bright enough to see by day if the observer knows exactly where to look. Let us begin when it is first seen soon after sunset, not very far from the sun. For several months it moves steadily further from the sun, sets later, and becomes a more prominent object. Then, when the angle between it and the sun is 47° it begins to move back towards the sun and in a few short weeks is lost again. It is in this latter period that it reaches its greatest brilliancy, many times brighter than the first magnitude and is said to be capable of causing shadows on the ground. Venus (at her best), sometimes known as Hesperus, the Evening Star, is probably the most beautiful object in the whole of the heavens. A few weeks later Lucifer, Son of the Morning, rises shortly before the sun and while rapidly reaching its maximum angle is again a brilliant object, though on account of the hour much less familiar. Finally it slowly falls back to the sun and the cycle starts again. Sometimes, at very long intervals—the last occasion was in 1882—a little black dot is seen moving over the face of the sun between the passing of Hesperus and the birth of Lucifer. This phenomenon is called a transit of Venus.

The other three naked eye planets, Mars, Jupiter and Saturn, behave rather differently. They can be brilliant objects, though not so fine as Venus, and Mars, the God of War, shines with a reddish light. Their cycle of movement is more like that of the stars. They appear first in the east in the morning sky, and as the months go by they rise earlier each day until they are on the Meridian, the north-south line, at midnight. It is at this time that they are at their brightest. Eventually they too vanish into the sunset glow. The planets are in steady motion with respect to their starry background, and for most of the time, like the moon, their motion is from west to east. About the time of greatest brilliancy, however, their motion is in the opposite direction, or retrograde. As will be shown in the next chapter, the ancient astronomers tried hard to explain these planetary motions, and the problem that gave them the greatest trouble was this mystery of the retrograde motion. In the course of time the planets move right around the sky and come back to the constellation in which they started. The order in which their names have occurred in this chapter is the order of increasing period; Saturn takes nearly 30 years to return to its starting point. Pluto, a little planet seen only with really large telescopes, takes about 250 years!

From time to time the night sky is visited by a comet, though for the last 40 years Britain has not been favoured with a spectacular one. A great comet, looking to the naked eye like the lower picture in Plate VII (p. 128), is a wonderful sight that made a great impression in early times. One appeared about the time of the death of

Fig. 4. The Comet in the Bayeux Tapestry. *Drawn by A. R. Steele*

Julius Caesar; of this Shakespeare writes 'When beggars die there are no comets seen; the heavens themselves blaze forth the death of princes'. Another appeared just before the Norman Conquest and is depicted in the Bayeux tapestry, Fig. 4. Usually however, a comet, if visible at all to the unaided eye, is just a hazy spot moving quite rapidly among the stars so that its changes can be followed from night to night. What are comets, and whence do they come? Another mystery to be elucidated later on.

Most people who go out at night have seen a shooting star, or meteor. Their appearance varies a great deal; some are bright, some faint; some trails are quite short and others long; some leave a trail of sparks, and some may even be heard. These objects are not stars at all, but are pieces of rock, sometimes with a high metallic content, flying very fast high in the earth's atmosphere. Their origin, like that of the comets, is a mystery to which we must return later. Sometimes they hit the ground with a loud explosion, and pieces of this meteorite that has come to us from far away in space can be picked up and examined. There are several known instances where a large meteorite has struck with a violence comparable with an atomic bomb, though fortunately such occurrences are rare. It is often thought that it is impossible to do any real astronomy without using a large telescope, but here is a field in which the amateur can and does do much valuable work with the unaided eye. Only by long and patient observation can the mystery of the meteors be solved, and the observer who knows the stars so well that he can spot the beginning and end of a trail almost by instinct can make a real contribution to science.

The Aurora, or Northern Lights, has been adequately treated elsewhere (1). It is a terrestrial phenomenon, but astronomical in origin, and is another realm of study in which the amateur astronomer makes a notable contribution.

Now go out and look at the sky; do not be content to do all your astronomy at the fireside with this book.

REFERENCES

(1) C. M. Botley, *The Air and its Mysteries*, 1938.
(2) *The Stars at a Glance*, published by George Philip & Sons, is recommended.

CHAPTER II

The Mysteries Attacked

WE read in Genesis Ch. XI that 'Terah took Abram his son . . . from Ur of the Chaldees, to go into the land of Canaan . . . ' and the date quoted in the margin is 1923 B.C. On their journey in that sub-tropical desert land the mysteries of the sky would be presented to them, and would not be unfamiliar because the country from which they came was the very cradle of astronomy. In the valley of the Euphrates, conveniently called the country of Babylonia, there flourished one of the earliest civilisations and we must just look briefly at their astronomical achievements (1), (2). One was the measurement of time. The day, and the month marked by the phases of the moon, were two obvious units and the difficulty was to reconcile these two with the year shown by the seasons. Their solution was a year of 360 days divided into 12 months. From time to time, as the seasons fell out of step, an extra month was added. The Babylonians were familiar with the motion among the stars of the sun, moon and the five planets and these seven moving bodies are a probable origin of a week of seven days. The sun and stars could not be seen at the same moment, of course, but the ancients did note what stars were visible near the sun at sunrise and sunset, and were thus able to plot the path of this body around the sky. This path is very much the same as that of the moon and planets, and the ancients well knew the band around the heavens in which all seven wanderers lay. This band was divided into 12 parts, one for each month, and they were named after mythical deities or animals, thus giving rise to the Signs of the Zodiac as we now know them. The movements of the heavenly bodies follow definite laws and repeat themselves at fixed intervals. These intervals were known in ancient times and the future aspects of the heavens were being predicted. It is believed that the Babylonians could predict eclipses as early as 600 B.C.; their astronomy as a whole goes back for some 2,000 years before Christ. Side by side with astronomy, astrology grew up, for these primitive people believed that human destiny was controlled by the stars, and it is probable that the corresponding wish to 'read the stars' was a main stimulant to the study of astronomy.

Egyptian civilisation was roughly contemporary with that of the Mesopotamian countries just considered, but their astronomy did not reach such a high level. One reason may be that the practical reason for studying the stars, astrology, meant less to them. Another may be that they did not keep records of their observations like the Chaldeans by the Euphrates, and were thus less able to profit by the experience of the past. The Egyptians had their constellation figures; these they used for decorative purposes and they have been handed down to us on coffin lids and ceilings of burial chambers. Like their contemporaries across the desert they also divided the sun's path, but into 36 parts instead of 12, for they divided their year into 36 weeks of 10 days each.

We must not forget two other ancient civilisations, those of India and China. In the case of the former it appears that astronomy was little studied in very ancient times, and certainly in no way comparable with Babylonia and Egypt. Science there was, but the main stream was in the realm of medicine. Indian astronomy came later, when the influence of the Greeks was already spreading eastward. Chinese records of astronomy, on the other hand, go back a very long way, though some authorities are not quite satisfied about their authenticity and research in China is not altogether easy for Europeans. Among very early records is one of a conjunction of several planets about 2446 B.C.; the path of the sun among the stars appears to have been mapped out by 2285 B.C. There is a story of two astronomers called Hi and Ho who were executed in 2159 B.C. for failing to predict an eclipse, though it is unlikely that eclipse predictions were possible as early as this. From 700 B.C. records become more reliable, and mention of comets and novae have proved useful to modern investigators. Sunspots were also known to the Chinese; the earliest known sunspot record (165 B.C.) is one of theirs (3). The stars were divided into 284 constellations, mostly small, but including Orion and the seven stars of the Plough—a bushel measure to them, c.f. the American 'dipper'. Thus in general the development of Chinese astronomy (4) was on similar lines to the Babylonian.

We may safely say that the primitive astronomers observed pretty well all that there was to observe from the lands in which they lived. They made, in some cases, practical use of it, in the Babylonian astrology for instance, in the orientation of the Egyptian pyramids, and the latter people used the rising of Sirius with the sun to mark the new year and the imminent rising of the Nile. They did little, however, to unravel the mystery, to answer the question 'why?' The Babylonian universe consisted of a flat world with the Euphrates as its central feature, surrounded by a moat, and covered with a ceiling to which the stars were attached. Other early cosmologies were similar, but with their own lands as the central feature. The ancient peoples gave us the constellations (5), but for progress towards the answer to the question 'why?' we must turn to the Greeks.

The Greeks took their astronomical facts very largely from Babylonia and subjected them to careful and imaginative examination. Thales of Miletus, working about 580 B.C., can be regarded as the pioneer theoretical scientist though his ideas as to the nature of the earth and sky were as primitive as the others. Anaximander went a little further and regarded the visible sky as a hemisphere; the earth floated in space at the middle with the sun, moon and stars revolving around it. His earth, however, was a cylinder with the known world, of which he had made a map, forming the circular end. He supposed that at night the sun went underground, which was a little nearer the truth than the earlier theory of the boat carrying the celestial fire behind the northern mountains. It seems to have been Pythagoras, of 'square on the hypoteneuse' fame, who really recognised that the earth was a sphere. He also proposed that the apparent motion of the heavenly bodies was due to the real motion of the earth. Unfortunately Plato, another great man of a slightly later period, rejected this latter idea and developed a system based on the fixed earth. He arranged the various astronomical bodies in their correct order of distance and he recognised that the motions of Venus and Mercury differ from the other planets. His theory was further developed by Eudoxus, who attempted to explain the planetary movements in detail by combining various circular motions of the transparent spheres to which the planets were attached. This was the state of knowledge at the time of Aristotle

(384-322 B.C.), 'the greatest collector and systematizer of knowledge which the ancient world produced' (1). So great was the authority of his writings that little progress in science was made for many centuries afterwards. One or two other points of interest may be mentioned before leaving the work of the Greeks. Aristarchus suggested about 250 B.C. that the earth revolved around the sun, but he was ahead of his time. Hipparchus produced a most valuable catalogue of the positions of the principal stars, and also classified the stars in their magnitudes. He attempted to measure the distance of the moon and found it to be 34 times the diameter of the earth. He also invented epicycles, explained below, as a substitute for the spheres of Eudoxus. About the same time Eratosthenes, the librarian at Alexandria, measured the circumference of the earth, Fig. 5. He observed that on a certain

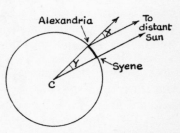

Fig. 5. Finding the circumference of the earth

date when the sun was vertically overhead at Syene it cast a shadow at Alexandria. The length of the shadow gave him the angle X, which is the same as Y, for the sun is so distant that the lines pointing to it can be taken as parallel. The distance between the two places was known, and since he had found Y to be a fiftieth of a circle the whole circumference could be found. Lastly we come to Ptolemy who in the second century A.D. produced a book, called the *Almagest*, in which he developed the earlier work of Hipparchus. His planets were moving in epicycles, i.e.

in a circle whose centre moves around the earth in another circle called the deferent, Fig. 7. He also produced a star catalogue similar to that of his predecessor, and obtained a value for the distance of the moon.

With Ptolemy we come to the end of the first phase in unravelling the mystery of the sky. Let us pause and consider how far we have got. First, the earth is a sphere, Fig. 6, and, whether we regard it as rotating on its axis,

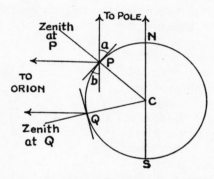

Fig. 6. The effect of latitude on the aspect of the sky

or stationary with the heavens rotating around it, some of the observations of Ch. I can be explained. In either case NS is the axis of rotation and owing to the distance of the stars the lines marked 'to pole' are parallel. Let the observer be at P; the tangent at that point is his horizon. Now any stars whose angular distance from the pole is not more than a will never go below that horizon and are therefore circumpolar. Similarly stars in the angle marked b will never rise. As P moves north the circumpolar circle becomes larger and may even include the sun. Moving southward, the circumpolar area becomes smaller, but the stars in angle *b* gradually come into view. Consider the direction of Orion, the constellation on the celestial equator, mid-way between the poles. Seen from P it is to the south of zenith, the overhead point, but from Q it is north of it. All these remarks are in agreement with the statements made in Ch. I and, it is hoped, verified by the reader.

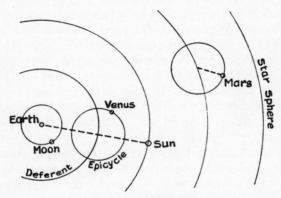

Fig. 7. The Ptolemaic system

Now for the planetary motions, Fig. 7. This is a simplified version of the Ptolemaic system; Mercury, which lies between the moon and Venus, is not shown, nor have Jupiter and Saturn been put in outside Mars. The sun appears to go round the earth once a day; let us suppose that it does so, from east to west. Then the star sphere will do so in four minutes less than day, giving the sun its apparent annual motion from west to east relative to the stars. The moon rises about 50 minutes later each night, so its orbit around the earth must take more than a day. Venus is moving in a circle the centre of which is always

in the line joining the earth and sun. This circle gives it
its motion to and fro across the sun; it is drawn east of
the sun, as an evening star, and if it were in the lower half
of the epicycle it would be a morning star. Mercury
behaves in the same way. The centres of the epicycles of
these two have the same period in their deferents as the
sun in its orbit, but the centre for Mars has a different
period so that its position relative to the sun changes.
The period in the epicycle is in this case the same as in
the deferent. When, from the earth, Mars is seen on the
far side of its epicycle its two motions will be in the same
direction and it will be moving among the stars particularly quickly, but when it is in the near side of the epicycle
it will temporarily seem to move in the opposite direction
—hence retrograde motion. Jupiter and Saturn are similar
to Mars. Very complicated, and this is the Ptolemaic
system in its simplest form!

The constellation figures were described by Aratus in
270 B.C. and were much the same as we see them now.
Some or all of them may have been taken over from the
earlier civilisations, but by the time they had been handed
on to later generations numerous Greek stories had been
attached to them. This is not the place to tell them (6),
(7), (8).

There is now a very long gap in the progress of astronomy. The introduction of new ideas was difficult because
the old ideas, as laid down by Aristotle, had become a
tradition, indeed almost a religious belief. We do not
feel the earth moving; therefore it does not move. Man
is God's greatest creation and must therefore occupy the
centre of the universe. Ptolemy's system enabled the
movements of the heavenly bodies to be predicted well
enough for the needs of the time. Anyone who challenged

these things did so at the risk of his life; Bruno believed that the earth moved, and went to the stake in 1600, though in his case he challenged the established order in other things as well.

Mikołaj Kopernik, better known as Copernicus, was born in 1473, his father being a Pole and his mother a German. He was trained in Cracow and afterwards studied in Italy, and although well versed in all the scientific learning of his time, astronomy and mathematics were his main interests. He was by profession a church official. He was dissatisfied with the extreme complication of the Ptolemaic system and had read of the suggestion at the time of Pythagoras that the apparent motion of the sky was due to the real motion of the earth. At the end of some 30 years' work he published in 1543, the year of his death, his great book *De Revolutionibus*. Here, at considerable length and detail, he pointed out how much more likely it was that the earth moved, both rotating on its axis and revolving around the sun. Using his own words (9): 'Most distant of all is the Sphere of the Fixed Stars, containing all things, and being therefore itself immovable. It represents that to which the motion and position of all the other bodies must be referred. Some hold that it too changes in some way, but we shall assign another reason for this apparent change, as will appear in the account of the Earth's motion. Next is the planet Saturn, revolving in 30 years. Next comes Jupiter, moving in a 12 year circuit; then Mars, who goes round in 2 years. The fourth place is held by the annual revolution in which the Earth is contained, together with the orbit of the Moon as on an epicycle. Venus, whose period is 9 months, is in the fifth place, and sixth is Mercury, who goes round in the space of 80 days. In the middle of all sits Sun enthroned.

In this most beautiful temple could we place this luminary
in any better position from which he can illuminate the
whole at once? He is rightly called the Lamp, the Mind,

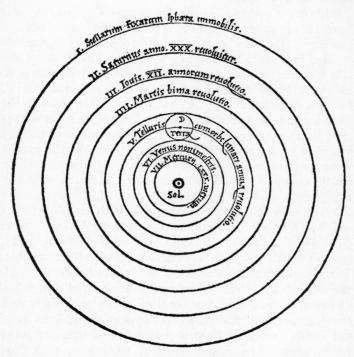

Fig. 8. The Copernican system as shown in *De Revolutionibus*

the Ruler of the Universe; . . .' His system is illustrated
in Fig. 8. Copernicus also anticipated some of the objections. If the earth were rotating, the clouds and other
detached objects would be left behind; no, for these are

of the earth and share its motion. It is common knowledge that if you move your head to and fro there is a relative movement among objects at various distances from you. The distant background moves with your head past the nearer object. This motion is called parallax. If the earth is moving to and fro about the sun, should not the stars show such motion? No, says Copernicus, for the stars are so distant that the parallactic effect is unnoticeable.

The work of Copernicus was not generally accepted, and Tycho Brahe (1545-1601) proposed a theory of his own. This is of no importance in comparison with the experimental work that he did. He received the patronage of the Danish court and was able to build an observatory at Uraniborg, where in the course of 20 years' work he measured the positions of the stars and planets with an accuracy never before achieved. With a change of king came a change of fortune, so he left Denmark and went to live under much reduced circumstances in Prague. Here he was joined by a younger man, Johann Kepler (1571-1630), a German. These two intended to use Tycho's experimental results to make new astronomical tables, but Tycho died before the work was completed. Kepler continued to work on these Rudolphine Tables, but became increasingly dissatisfied with the systems of Tycho and Ptolemy that he was using. He was a mathematician who believed that mathematical simplicity and beauty was one of the purposes of God in the creation, so he scrapped the old systems and turned his attention to reconciling the experimental results of Tycho with the theory of Copernicus. As a result he discovered three laws of planetary motion. The first of these is that the orbit of a planet is not a circle but an ellipse, having the sun at one of its foci. An ellipse is a curve such that the sum of

c

the distances from the two foci to any part of it is always the same. Fig. 9 shows a simple way of drawing one; the pins are the foci and their distance apart determines whether the resulting oval will be elongated or nearly a circle. The orbits of the planets are of the latter kind. The second law was that the line from the sun to the planet called the radius vector sweeps over equal areas in equal times, Fig. 10. Thus, when the planet is at peri-

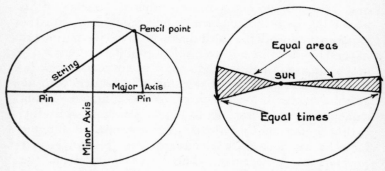

Fig. 9.   Drawing an ellipse   *Fig. 10.*   Kepler's second law

helion, the point nearest to the sun, it is moving faster than at aphelion. Finally the third law provided a link between the behaviour of the several planets. It stated that the squares of the periods taken to revolve around the sun are directly proportional to the cubes of the mean distances from the sun. The Copernican system in its original form was based upon circles; it was now modified by the introduction of the ellipse and at last there was a theory that was both simple and accurate.

The first two laws were published in 1609 (the third came later), a year in which another astronomical milestone was being laid elsewhere, for a Dutch spectacle-maker invented or accidentally discovered the telescope. This came to the ears of Galileo (1564-1642), a distinguished philosopher in Italy. He had already shown himself to be an experimental physicist of a high order and in a very short time he had made such an instrument and turned it to the sky. With Galileo's publication in 1610 a new era of astronomy had begun. He found that the planet Jupiter had four attendant bodies, or satellites, that could be watched night after night circulating around the central body—a perfect working model of the Copernicus-Kepler solar system. He saw that Venus shows phases like the moon. Examination of Fig. 7 will show that in the Ptolemaic system it would never be possible to see more than half the illuminated face of the planet, which shines by reflected sunlight, whereas in reality it goes through a full cycle of phases, in agreement with the new theory. Other discoveries were the mountains on the moon, the starry nature of the Milky Way, the disk-like appearance of a planet in contrast with the indefinable point of light due to a star, and the discovery of sunspots coupled with the added fact of their rotation about the axis of the sun. Needless to say Galileo's work in this and other fields was not popular either with Church or University, for it disturbed so much of the centuries-old belief. He was brought before the Inquisition in 1633, forced to make a statement denying his discoveries, and spent the rest of his life quietly under a form of house arrest.

One great mystery of the sky has now been unravelled, and at this stage we must pause and take stock. At the centre of the system we have the luminous sun, around it circulate the several planets of which the earth is the third, and then, at distances very great compared with those of the planets, lie the stars. Study Fig. 11A, which shows the orbits of the earth and one of the two inner planets. As they have a shorter period than a year they gain on the earth, Venus for instance gaining one whole revolution in 584 days. For simplicity suppose that the earth is at rest and Venus moving around its orbit in 584

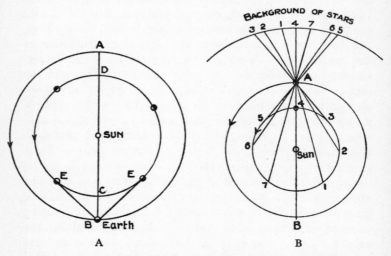

Fig. 11. Aspects of the planets: A. Inner planets; B. Outer planets

days. When it lies along AB it is said to be in conjunction and cannot be seen. When to the left of the diagram it is east of the sun and would be seen in the evenings, while on the right we have the morning star. At E the planet is at its greatest elongation from the sun and we should see it half illuminated. Along the path ECE we should see only a crescent, whereas along EDE its appearance is more than half. The brightest apparition of the planet occurs in the crescent phase because it is so much nearer at that time. Fig. 11B shows one of the outer planets. It is drawn at the time of opposition, when it is on the opposite side of the earth from the sun and is at its nearest and brightest. Its steady motion along its orbit would carry it eastwards against the background of stars, but the more rapid revolution of the earth will add to this an oscillatory motion shown by following the figures on the earth's orbit and the corresponding ones on the background. It will be seen that at opposition the planet has the retrograde motion that we noted in Ch. I and which gave rise to the epicycles of Hipparchus and his successors. For a complete diagram the reader is referred to any good atlas. Here it will be found that there are more planets than have so far been mentioned, so we must now resume the story and find out how the new ones came to be discovered.

As one great man passed away another came into the world; towards the end of the year in which Galileo died there was born in a Lincolnshire village Isaac Newton (1642-1727). He went to Cambridge in 1661 and studied experimental science and mathematics. It was in 1665 that he comes into this story, for the Great Plague had driven him out of Cambridge to his country home. Here, it is popularly believed, the fall of an apple led him to speculate on the cause of the moon's motion. It is one of the characteristics of science that the solution of one problem so often presents another. We have seen that the ancient astronomers knew how the planets move in the sky but made no real attempt to find out why they so move. Kepler and Galileo answered that question; because they move around the sun in accordance with Kepler's laws. The new problem was why do they move around the sun? Since the moon is moving in an orbit, around the earth it must all the time be falling towards the earth, i.e., there must be a force towards the earth acting upon it. It is common knowledge that if a weight is swung round at the end of a string the pull on the string can be felt, and if the string breaks the weight flies off at a tangent. Any unsupported object near the earth falls to the ground; there is an attractive force, investigated by Galileo, acting upon it. Newton's problem was: could the force holding the moon in its orbit be of the same nature as the force acting on the falling body? If this is so, if two bodies attract one another, it follows from Kelper's third law that the force is inversely proportional to the square of the distance between them, i.e. if the distance be doubled the force is reduced to one quarter, three times the distance gives one ninth of the force, and so on. Working from this hypothesis, Newton calculated the acceleration of the moon towards the earth and thence deduced what the acceleration of the falling body should be. His result was in good agreement with the known acceleration of such bodies, but owing to some difficulties and uncertainties he was not fully satisfied, and it was not until 1687 that his work was published in his great book, the *Principia*. The law of gravitation is that every particle attracts every other particle with a force that is directly proportional to the product of their masses and inversely proportional to the square of the distance between them. The 'distance' means the distance between their centres of gravity, large bodies behaving towards external objects as if all their mass were concentrated at one point which for uniform spheres is the geometrical centre. In order to calculate the actual numerical value of the force it is necessary to know a number called the constant of gravitation, and it was not until a century later that this constant was determined. In addition to his work on gravitation and mechanics Newton made a systematic investigation of the colours produced when light passes through a glass prism, and invented a new type of tele-scope, the first of which is now preserved in the rooms of the Royal Society. This work can be studied more conveniently in the next chapter.

Sir Isaac Newton was one of the greatest English men of learning who ever lived, and he lived in a period that was rich in learning. In his own country there were Hooke, a keen and critical intellect applied to many branches of science; Wren, the famous architect; and Halley, who predicted the return of the comet of 1682 now known by his name. Nor must we forget Huygens of the Hague, who improved the telescope and showed that Saturn had rings; and Roemer, the Dane, who from ob-servations of Jupiter's satellites deduced the velocity of light to be about 186,000 miles a second. In 1662 the Royal Society was formed under the charter of Charles II, and the same king founded the Royal Observatory at Greenwich in 1675. It was built by Wren and the first Astronomer Royal was John Flamsteed (1646-1720), whose work was to make the observations necessary for the improvement of navigation; he was the father of English observational astronomy. On his death he was succeeded by Halley. Under such men as these astronomy made rapid progress, but what about those other planets men-tioned a few pages back?

On the 13th of March 1781 William Herschel was examining the stars in the constellation of Taurus when he found one that looked abnormal. He called it 'nebul-ous' and thought that it might be a comet. During the few days following he found that it was changing its position, and announced his discovery. Further observations were made and the mathematicians, armed with the weapon provided by Newton, set to work to calculate its orbit. It was found to be a planet beyond the orbit of Saturn, too faint to observe without a telescope, and was named Uranus.

Herschel was a German who had settled in England as a musician; he worked in Bath as a teacher and organist. As a hobby he made telescopes and, assisted by his faithful sister Caroline, used them to some effect. After the discovery of Uranus he became a professional astronomer, settled in Slough, and in due course became Sir William. It will now be convenient to break the chronological order of this chapter and continue the pursuit of planets; Herschel's other work will be considered later.

As the years went by observations of Uranus accumulated, and by examining star maps made before 1781 a number of earlier positions were found, going back as far as 1690. Unfortunately a calculated orbit that would fit the early values would not account for the recent ones, and the first and obvious solution to this puzzle was to assume that the early ones were not good enough to use. By 1830, however, the observed positions did not agree with predictions based on the newer readings alone. Some suggested that the orbit had been changed by a collision with a comet; others that Newton's law of gravitation did not hold for distances as great as that of Uranus; and some that Uranus was being disturbed by the gravitational attraction, or perturbation, of another planet still unknown. This latter solution caught the attention, in 1841, of a brilliant mathematical student at Cambridge, J. C. Adams, who resolved to attack the problem when his studies were completed. This he did, and in September 1845 he reached his solution and could predict the position of the new planet for any particular date. He proceeded to inform Airy, the Astronomer Royal, but unfortunately no immediate steps were taken to find the planet (10). Meanwhile a French astronomer, Le Verrier, was tackling the same problem, and a solution similar to that of Adams was published by him in June 1846. In July Airy asked Challis to search for the planet, using the great telescope at Cambridge. There was in Cambridge, however, no detailed star map of the area of sky concerned, so work was put in hand to make one. In September Le Verrier asked Galle in Berlin to search for his planet; Galle had the necessary map, and on September 23rd the planet was found. Examination of Challis' work showed that he had seen it, without recognising it, on August 4th. Whose planet was it? A lively situation at the time, but now both names are coupled with the discovery of Neptune.

Neptune remained the outermost planet for many years, but the perturbations of Uranus, even when Neptune had been allowed for, were not fully explained even yet. By 1915 an American astronomer, Percival Lowell, had concluded that there was yet another planet, beyond Neptune, and computed an orbit for it. The search at the time was unsuccessful, but in 1930 Tombaugh, another American, found it by a photographic method. Pluto is a very faint object and was assumed to be comparable in size with the earth. Recent work suggests that it is too small to be responsible for the perturbations that led to its discovery, so it seems that the mystery of the motion of Uranus is still with us.

There is an interesting series of numbers, known as Bode's Law, though they had been noticed before his time.

Begin with the series, 0, 3, 6, 12, and so on, each being double the preceding. To each add 4, making 4, 7, 10, 16, 28, 52, etc. Underneath these write the distances of the planets from the sun in 'astronomical units', i.e. calling the distance of the earth 1 unit. These will be 0·39, 0·72, 1·00, 1·52, 5·2, etc. If these be multiplied by ten they would look very similar to the series of numbers, except, of course, the 28. Here is the whole table:

Mercury	Venus	Earth	Mars	?	Jupiter	Saturn	Uranus	Neptune	Pluto
0	3	6	12	24	48	96	192	384	768
4	7	10	16	28	52	100	196	388	772
3·9	7·2	10	15·2	—	52	95·4	192	301	396

The agreement is quite good as far as Uranus, and then breaks down. The point of interest is the gap at 28; ought there to be another planet there? Bode organised a search for a possible planet, though the first success was an accidental one. Piazzi in 1801 found a moving object just below naked eye visibility, and when Gauss calculated its probable orbit its mean distance from the sun turned out to be 2·77, just what was wanted to fill the gap at No. 28. It is a very small planet called Ceres. In 1802 another little planet was found to suit this distance, and 1804 a third, and in 1807 yet another! The number of Minor Planets or Asteroids remained at four until 1845, and after that more were discovered with ever-increasing rapidity; there are now about 2,000 and we do not seem to have got to the end of them yet.

We now return to Sir William Herschel, settled in Slough as a professional astronomer and doing a prodigious amount of work (11). With better telescopes than had ever been used before, he studied everything. He watched the sun's surface and tried to correlate it with terrestrial weather; he had ideas about the physical constitution of the sun. He attempted to measure the heights of the lunar mountains. He saw a transit of Mercury over the disk of the sun. He tried to determine the period of rotation of Venus upon its axis, and succeeded in finding that of Mars; he also saw the snowcaps and changing seasons on the latter. He studied Jupiter and Saturn, and found two moons for his own planet Uranus. His great contribution to science, however, was beyond the solar system altogether; he was the founder of stellar astronomy. Four times, with ever increasing optical aid, he searched the whole northern heavens, discovering Uranus while making his second examination. There are visible to the naked eye a number of hazy spots of faint light called nebulae, and many more are visible with a telescope. Messier had recently published a catalogue of 103 of the objects; Herschel raised the number to about 2,500, some of which his telescope resolved into clusters of individual stars. If you examine the middle star of the handle of the Plough you will see that it has a close companion; it is a naked eye pair. Many stars are found to be double when examined with a telescope of sufficient power; Herschel listed about 800 of these. By comparing star positions of his own time with earlier ones he noted that the so-called fixed stars were moving slowly among themselves, and from these results he deduced that the sun is moving through space and taking its planets with it. He made star counts for different areas of the sky and proposed a theory of the distribution of stars in space; to this we shall refer in a later chapter. He died in 1822. How the field of astronomy had widened in 200 years!

Sir John Herschel (1792-1871) carried on his father's work, particularly for the southern hemisphere, spending some years in Cape Colony for this purpose. He added several hundred nebulae to his father's list, and examined over 2,000 double stars.

While William Herschel was developing the observational side of astronomy to a degree never before attempted a contemporary in France, Laplace (1749-1827), was working on the mathematical side. In this field he cleared up numerous irregularities in the motions of the solar family, and did some valuable work on calculating the tides. Herschel, we have seen, attacked the question of the shape of system of the stars; Laplace was famous for his attempt to explain how the planets came into existence. Both these men were looking ahead, for these problems belong to our own time. Astronomy was now advancing on a broad front and it will no longer be possible to discuss it in chronological order. Each aspect will require a chapter to itself. There are, however, one or two important milestones that must be briefly mentioned before closing this chapter.

Mention has already been made of Newton's work on the spectrum, the band of colour produced when white light passes through a prism. The spectrum of sunlight has crossing it a number of dark lines. These lines were carefully examined and recorded by Fraunhofer in 1814 and have since borne his name. It was not until another 40 years had elapsed that the nature of the lines was fully understood, but their original examination is an event of historic significance as Fraunhofer's lines ultimately became the key to unlock the mystery of starlight.

Hitherto investigators like the Herschels knew the content of space but not its scale. Copernicus had pointed out that the stars were vastly more distant than the sun, and the measurements of the solar system had been known with moderate accuracy since 1700—the distance of the sun was about 90 million miles, some observers having got rather less and others rather more—but the distances of the stars could only be guessed. Copernicus had also pointed out that the parallax of a star was exceedingly small; Herschel tried to measure it. Herschel thought that an unequal double star was a near star and a distant one in nearly the same line of sight, and proceeded to look for relative motion between them. He failed to determine the parallax because most double stars really are a pair at the same distance from us, but he did discover that some doubles are in motion around one another. The proper motion of the stars among themselves has been referred to; assuming that on the average their real velocities are the same, a relatively rapid motion would indicate a near star. This led Bessel to study the star called 61 Cygni, and in 1838 it had yielded up its secret: its distance was about 64 million million miles. The angle of parallax to be measured was only one third of a second of arc,* and as one second is the apparent size of a tennis ball eight miles away it is not surprising that the opponents of Copernicus could not observe it! Two more stars were successfully determined by other investigators in the next two years.

The inventor of the first practical system of photography, Daguerre, made the first astronomical photograph, an eclipse of the sun, in 1839, and during the next decade several experimenters obtained successful 'daguerrotypes' of the moon, the sun with sunspots, the spectrum of sunlight, and of the images of one or two bright stars. Photographic methods have become so important that 1839 must rank as a date to remember.

* 1 degree (1°) = 60 minutes (60′).
  1 minute   = 60 seconds (60″).

Lastly, in 1845, the Earl of Rosse completed his telescope at Parsonstown (now Birr) in Ireland. It was far larger than any previous instrument, being 6 feet in diameter and 52 feet long; it was difficult to handle and was limited in range to stars near the meridian. With this telescope some of the nebulae were found to have a spiral structure. This in itself does not appear to be a milestone in astronomy, but the recognition of this kind of nebula as a separate class is important. One can almost say that these objects lie 'beyond the stars', for they are at distances up to a million or more times greater than 61 Cygni. Herschel imagined the stars to occupy a disklike volume in space that we now call the Galaxy. These nebulae, recognised in 1845 as something different, are other galaxies far outside our own; at one bound the universe expanded to something greater than had been believed since the time of Bruno, who said that it was infinite.

Up to this time astronomy had been largely local and positional. Fixing the positions of the stars and planets; studying the laws of motion that they obeyed; predicting their future positions; these had been the main line of advance. The surfaces of the various members of the solar system were studied of course, Herschel had opened up stellar astronomy, and Fraunhofer and his successors had discovered a valuable means of physical attack, but the emphasis still remained on the mechanical side. It was a mechanical age and there was a tendency to reduce all scientific theory to a machine of some kind. The mental picture conjured up by the words 'solar system' was the Orrery, a model with which the motion of the planets could be imitated by turning a handle. It is difficult to say just when the change came about, but the astronomical emphasis in the twentieth century is on the stellar and physical side; the problem is not '*where* is that planet?' but '*what* is that star?' In the latter part of the nineteenth century steady progress was made in improving instruments and methods, leading up to the modern equipment that must now be described.

REFERENCES

(1) Sir Williams Dampier, *A History of Science*, 1929 (brief reference).

(2) Peter Doig, *A Concise History of Astronomy*, 1950 (fuller treatment).

(3) D. J. Schove, *Journal of the B.A.A.*, 61/22, 1950.

(4) Summarised by H. Chatley in *Occasional Notes of the R.A.S.*, 1/65, 1939.

(5) Described by A. C. D. Crommelin in Hutchinson's *Splendour of the Heavens*, Ch. 17, 1925.

(6) E. A. Beet, *A Guide to the Sky*, 1950, gives some of them briefly.

(7) They are given more fully in Mary Procter's *Evenings with the Stars*, 1924.

(8) Sir William Peck, *Introduction to the Celestial Sphere*, Vol. 1, 1919; a formal guide to constellation mythology

(9) From Prof. J. F. Dobson's translation: *Occasional Notes of the R.A.S.*, II/1, 1947.

(10) The full story is told by W. M. Smart in *Occasional Notes of the R.A.S.*, II/33, 1947.

(11) An outline of his various papers is given by J. E. Gore, *Astronomical Essays*, Ch. X, 1907.

CHAPTER III

The Astronomers' Tools and Methods

The Telescope

EVERYONE is familiar with the ordinary convex lens, and many people have used it as a burning glass. You will therefore already know that a parallel beam of light from the sun or other distant object is gathered together to a point called the focus. If the light is not coming

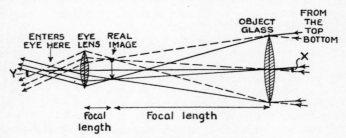

Fig. 12. The principle of the telescope

straight through the lens, i.e. parallel to its axis and perpendicular to its plane, it will meet at a point above or below the principal focus but in the focal plane. Fig. 12 shows three rays from a point at the top of the object; as the object is distant compared with the diameter of the object glass they are parallel rays and meet in the focal plane. The dotted lines are coming from the bottom of the object and also meet in the focal plane. Rays from the rest of the object will behave in the same way, and will

48

meet somewhere between the two limiting points shown. Thus in the focal plane there will be a complete but inverted reproduction of the object: this is the real image. Now if a magnifying glass, here called the eye lens, is used to look at this image a telescope in its simplest form has been achieved. Notice that the rays from the top and bottom of the object make the small angle X with each other when they enter the telescope, and the larger angle

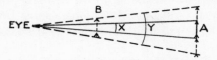

Fig. 13. Apparent size of a distant object

Y when they leave it. Now refer to Fig. 13. Our estimate of the size of an object depends upon the angle subtended at the eye by that object. Thus the apparent size of the object A depends on the angle X. If X suddenly grows to Y one of two things must have happened, either A has grown (dotted line) or has moved nearer into position B. Thus if a telescope enlarges the angle by 10, the object will appear 10 times as large, or at a tenth of the distance, according to taste. If a magnification of 1,000 were used to view the moon, objects on that body would look 1,000 times as big, or the moon would appear to be only 240 miles away instead of 240,000.

If you looked at the star 61 Cygni with this telescope it would look 1,000 times nearer, i.e. you would knock off three noughts from its distance, but as it happens to have 12 noughts the difference would be undetectable. You cannot magnify a star, and in fact for a tiny point object like this we are not really justified in using the above argument at all. It can be proved quite simply that the

D

ratio of Y to X is equal to the focal length of the object glass divided by that of the eye lens. Thus object glasses have long focal lengths and eye lenses have short ones.

Practical telescopes are more complicated than this. A simple lens does not give a perfect image, as camera users will probably know, and the shorter the focal length of the lens in comparison with its diameter the more serious is the trouble. A discussion on spherical aberration would be out of place in this book, so we will just point out that the eyepiece is made from two lenses some little distance apart in order to reduce this fault and the next one. When

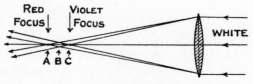

Fig. 14.   Chromatic aberration

light is refracted through glass, lens as well as prism, it is dispersed into colours as shown by Newton. The effect of this in the case of the object glass is illustrated in Fig. 14, where violet light comes to a focus nearer the lens than the red, and with all the other colours in between. At A we should expect to get a red spot with a violet ring around it, at B an approximately white disk, and at C a violet point with a red ring. Nowhere do we get a sharp white focus. This fault is called chromatic aberration and a lens free from it is an achromatic lens. Such a lens is made of two parts placed in contact and of two different kinds of glass. By this means the two strongest colours can be brought to the same focus, which two depending on the intended use of the telescope. Yellow and green are two most suitable for a visual telescope and blue and violet for photography. By using three components, three colours can be brought together, making a photo-visual instrument for either purpose. The two components in the eyepiece are chosen to make that achromatic also. Thus a refracting telescope consists of an object glass made of two components in contact and of long focal length, and an eyepiece of two separated components. It gives an inverted image, and a magnification equal to the ratio of the focal lengths. Its length is approximately the sum of the focal lengths of object glass and eyepiece.

You may think that you can make the magnification as great as you please by taking a very long focal length for one lens and a very short one for the other. The long one is, of course, limited by the need to manipulate the telescope conveniently, and the short one is limited by technical difficulties. There are, however, limitations of another kind to the useful magnification that can be employed. Let us consider what the instrument is required to do; there are two distinct cases. First consider an object of finite size like the disk of Jupiter, from which a certain quantity of light will enter the telescope. The larger the image produced the less bright it will be. If you have a brilliant object like the sun this does not matter very much, in fact you will be removing some in any case by dark shades or other means, but with an object like Jupiter it matters a great deal. It is no use magnifying the image so much that it is too faint to see. If a large magnifying power is needed, then it is not sufficient to have a long focal length only, but also a large diameter to let in an adequate quantity of light. Now consider a star image, which cannot be magnified in any case. Here the telescope is acting like a funnel, and all the light entering the telescope of aperture, say 3 inches, is poured into the pupil of the eye of diameter $\frac{1}{5}$ inch. Ratio 15:1; ratio of areas 225:1; hence the star will look (theoretically) 225 times brighter. The value of this is obvious, for it will enable you to see with the telescope stars that were too faint to see without. Some light is lost in transmission through the telescope, so the factor would not in practice be as much as 225. If you are looking at a pair of stars close together, then the magnification becomes effective, and widens them out enough for you to distinguish them separately. Thus for seeing faint stars you require a large diameter; power (magnification) is less important. We must also remember that the greater the power the less the field of view, or area of sky that we can see.

There is yet another limiting factor that applies to both cases, the ability to show fine detail. This is called re-solving power, and the limit is due to the wave nature of light. If two components of a double star are one second of arc apart, no magnification whatever could separate them with a 3 inch telescope; it is a physical impossibility for that telescope to distinguish objects closer than about 1·6 seconds, and to do that would require very high quality and perfect seeing. A 12 inch object glass could deal with double stars down to 0·4 second, for resolving power is dependent on the diameter. Thus once again the demand is for aperture. The length of the refracting telescopes vary, but as a rough idea we may take them to be about 15 times the diameter, which implies that they require strong and steady mountings, with an observatory to house them in the case of the larger ones.

The simplest arrangement that will give access to all parts of the sky is one having horizontal and vertical axes of rotation. This is called an altazimuth, and is commonly used for small portable instruments. It need not be further considered, as we are primarily concerned with observatory telescopes.

The first is for positional astronomy, the transit telescope or meridian circle, Fig. 15, which is diagrammatic and does not represent any particular instrument. The telescope is mounted on trunnions like an old fashioned

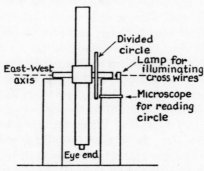

Fig. 15. The transit telescope

cannon and can move up and down along the meridian but cannot move east or west. It marks the meridian at the observatory. When an object crosses the meridian it is said to be in transit, and the interval between two successive transits of the sun is one solar day. The interval for a star is one sidereal day and is four minutes shorter. The sidereal day can be divided into hours and minutes, and a clock working on this principle is a sidereal clock. There is a certain point in the sky called the first point of Aries, and when this is on the meridian the sidereal clock should read 0 h. 0 m. All stars which are on the meridian at this same instant are said to have a Right Ascension of 0 h. 0 m. Suppose some other star is in transit 2 h.

25 m. later; its R.A. is said to be 2 h. 25 m. Thus the time
of transit by the sidereal clock and observed with the
transit circle fixes in part the position of the star on the
celestial sphere. The other measurement necessary to give
a definite fix is called Declination. All points 90° from
the pole lie on the celestial equator. Declination is the
angle of the star north or south of this equator, and can
be measured with the divided circle on this instrument.
Lines of R.A. and Dec. are shown on star maps and are
used in the same way as Long. and Lat. on ordinary maps.
The principle (but not the detail) of the use of the transit
circle is this. Shortly before the transit is due the telescope
is set to the right altitude and the observer goes to the
eyepiece to watch it. There are cross wires in the eyepiece,
and a little light is shone into the telescope tube so that
the observer can see them. When the star comes into view
he adjusts the altitude so that the star is exactly on the
horizontal wire, and starts his stop-watch when it crosses
the vertical wire. He then compares his watch with the
sidereal clock to get the R.A., and reads the microscopes
(only one shown) to find the Dec. Modern practice is to
do the timing automatically. The observer keeps the star
constantly on a movable vertical cross wire under his
control, and while he is doing so readings are automatically
recorded, together with the ticks of the clock, on a paper
sheet in an apparatus called a chronograph. Thus the
transit instrument can be used to find the position of a
star provided that correct time is known; conversely, if the
position of the star is known the clock can be corrected.
It is used for both purposes.

The normal observatory mounting is the equatorial,
which not only can be pointed in any direction but will
follow a star mechanically as it moves across the sky from

east to west. It is shown diagrammatically in Fig. 16A. There are two axes of rotation. AB, called the polar axis, is directed towards the celestial pole, so for readers in the northern hemisphere north is to the right of the diagram. Perpendicular to the polar axis is the declination axis CD; C itself is a counterpoise to balance the telescope when the polar axis rotates. Imagine the telescope to rotate

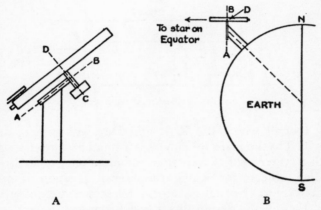

Fig. 16. The equatorial telescope

through 90° about CD so that the eye end comes out of the paper towards the reader; since it was pointing to the pole before, it must now be pointing to the celestial equator, and is also pointing west. Now imagine 90° rotation about AB so that the counterpoise goes back through the paper; the telescope is still pointing at the equator, but to the south, and in the position drawn in Fig. 16B. The earth rotates about the axis NS. If the telescope rotates in the opposite direction about the parallel axis AB and at the same rate it will continue to point to the same place on the celestial sphere. The axis AB is provided with a mechanical drive, still called the driving clock, even if it is electric, so that once the observer has set the telescope on the desired object it should follow it without further effort on his part; minor corrections are sometimes necessary in practice. Both axes are provided with divided circles so that the telescope can be directed to

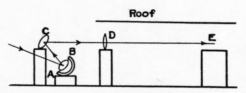

Fig. 17. A fixed solar telescope

any spot of which the R.A. and Dec. are known, and attached to the main tube there is a small finder telescope, with a larger field of view than the main one, to facilitate finding objects for which the known position is only approximate. Not all equatorial telescopes are quite like this, though the design illustrated is the commonest, but they all have these two motions. In the southern hemisphere the polar axis points to the south celestial pole so that south would be to the right of the diagram.

Now we come to a telescope which does not move at all. They are built horizontally in permanent or temporary buildings, or vertically in towers, or even down a well! The first is shown diagrammatically in Fig. 17, and is the kind of telescope that is rigged up on the site when parties go to an outlandish place to study an eclipse—indeed these telescopes are primarily intended for solar work. A mirror called a coelostat is mechanically rotated about

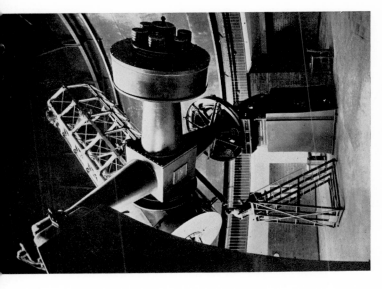

74 inch reflector at the Radcliffe Observatory, S. Africa
Howard Grubb, Parsons

40 inch refractor at the Yerkes Observatory, U.S.A.
Yerkes Observatory

II

Mount Palomar Observatory, U.S.A. *Palomar Photograph*

200 inch Hale telescope. *Palomar Photograph*

a polar axis AB, and the light of the sun is reflected in a fixed direction on to the mirror C. This second mirror, which has universal adjustments, deflects the light into the object glass D and thence to the observing apparatus E. There is no telescope tube and all the components are reasonably small for transport.

Nothing has been said about the size of refracting telescopes. Amateurs use from 3 to 8 inch; anything beyond about 4 inch requires an observatory with its revolving dome or equivalent, and by the time 12 inch telescopes are reached this is becoming quite large and expensive. Observatories use various sizes from 6 inch upwards, their larger refractors being in the 24 to 30 inch category; Greenwich has a 26 and a 28. The largest one in the world is at the Yerkes Observatory, University of Chicago, and is 40 inches in diameter and about 60 feet long. It is illustrated in Plate I (p. 56); note the equatorial mounting, the revolving dome, and the rising floor to bring the observer to eyepiece level when studying objects at low altitude. The telescope was made in 1897, and although a dozen or so large refractors have been made since, its size has never been equalled. The manufacture of a very large lens naturally presents difficulties. Light must pass through it; therefore the glass must be optically uniform all through. The lens must be supported by the edge; in consequence it may distort a little under its own weight as the telescope swings from one position to another. These faults are less serious if the glass is to be used as a mirror, for provided that the surface is good, minor irregularities inside are not important, and the mirror can be given all the support that it needs from the back. Thus telescopes exceeding 40 inches, and a great many smaller ones, employ mirrors in place of large lenses.

Reflecting Telescopes

The general principle of this kind of telescope is the same as before, but in place of the object glass, there is a concave mirror which, like the object glass, forms a real image in its focal plane where it is viewed with an eyepiece. The light does not penetrate the mirror and is therefore neither refracted nor dispersed; the mirror is achromatic. It was this characteristic that led Newton to

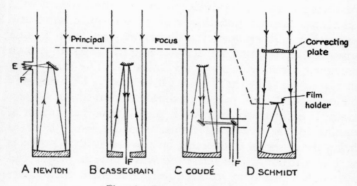

Fig. 18. Four types of reflector

devise the first reflector, and his layout, still in general use, is shown in Fig. 18A. Note the small flat mirror to divert the reflected beam out of the tube. This does not blot out the middle of the field of view as some people seem to expect, for every part of the main mirror makes a contribution to every part of the image and the presence of an obstruction reduces its brightness but not its extent. The eyepiece, if used, would be at E and photographs would be taken at F, or where F would be if the flat were removed. The surface of the concave mirror is not spherical, because such a mirror would give a point focus and hence a perfect image only if the focal length is very long compared with the diameter. The shape therefore is a parabola; a motor headlamp is approximately parabolic, but of course the astronomer's mirror is using only the extreme back of the curve and is very nearly flat. The large mirrors of the last century, such as the six foot one at Parsonstown, were made of an alloy of copper and tin called speculum. They are now made of glass, usually the pyrex variety, and silvered on the upper surface. As the silvering is exposed to the atmosphere the deposit has to be renewed from time to time. A modern development is the use of aluminium for the coating. This does not need renewing so often and is a very good reflector for photographic purposes.

Fig. 18 shows two other ways of dealing with the reflected beam. In B the flat has been replaced by a convex mirror which sends the light back down the tube and through a hole in the main mirror. In C there is again a convex mirror, though of a different curvature, and two flats, so that the light is directed into the polar axis of the mounting. This enables the light to be examined with apparatus that would be too heavy to use on a moving telescope. Through the sequence of A, B and C the effective focal length is increasing, and with it the size of the primary image and hence the possible magnification. Discussion of Fig. 18 D will be deferred for the moment.

A modern reflector of conventional pattern is the 74 inch of the Radcliffe Observatory in South Africa (1), (2). This observatory was formerly at Oxford, but in 1936 the move began to a new site in the southern hemisphere and shortly afterwards the telescope was ordered. It was nearly finished on the outbreak of war, when work came to a standstill. The telescope is still not quite complete but has been in use in the Newtonian form for some time. In Plate I (p. 56), note the polar axis supported on two pillars, the enormous counterpoise, the mounting for the Newtonian eyepiece, the hole in the main mirror, and the finder telescope in front of the observer. The driving mechanism is electric. The main mirror has a focal length of 30 feet, but when used as a Cassegrain or Coudé the equivalent focal length increases to 111 and 173 feet respectively. In the last case the light goes down the polar axis into a small laboratory at its lower end, the little brick building visible in the photograph. A travelling gantry fitted to the wall above the railings gives access to the eyepiece at the top of the tube. To accommodate this gantry the usual dome is missing and the observatory building is cylindrical.

An unfortunate weakness of the orthodox reflector is that perfect definition is obtained only very close to the axis. For the visual observation of, say, a planet, this does not matter, but for a more extended object it becomes serious. With the Radcliffe telescope it was intended to use the Newtonian focus for photography on quarter-plates, which are only $3\frac{1}{4} \times 4\frac{1}{4}$ inches—this small field in a 74 inch mirror. A correcting lens was designed to enable photographs to be made rather larger, 16 cm. square. We have seen how a large aperture gives a brighter image, and how a long focal length gives a larger but fainter image. It is clear, then, that for the examination and photography of very faint objects a large aperture and short focal length are both required. The field of view will be larger and the magnification small, but if the photograph is a perfect one it can be enlarged afterwards. The average refractor was stated to have a length of about

15 times the diameter, i.e. the aperture is about $\frac{1}{15}$ of the focal length, described as in photography as f/15. The Radcliffe as a Newtonian would have an aperture of about f/5. To obtain a better photographic telescope than this we should require an even shorter focal length, which would be very difficult to make in parabolic form because the hollow to be rubbed out of it would be getting rather deep. Even if it were made, we still could not have both the perfect definition and the larger field of view. The answer to this problem was given by Bernhard Schmidt (1879-1935) in 1930, Fig. 18 D. The mirror is spherical, which is easier to make than parabolic, and to correct for its defects there is at twice the focal length a plate of glass. It is nearly a parallel plate, but has been ground to the form shown in cross section in the diagram; to show it in the diagram the variation in thickness has been magnified at least 100 times. Schmidt's first such instrument had an aperture of f/1·75 with a 44 cm. mirror and a 36 cm. plate. Numerous such instruments have been made since the war, one being illustrated in Plate III (p. 96). The large image produced is not flat, but curved; either the film can be stretched over a curved former as shown, or additional optical parts can be introduced to give the picture on flat plates (3), (4), (5).

Reflecting telescopes increased in size step by step. Herschel reached 4 feet in 1789 and Rosse 6 feet in 1845, though these were rather before their time, and 36 inches was a large telescope in the nineteenth century; 60 inches was reached in 1903 and 100 inches in 1917, the latter being the famous Mount Wilson telescope that remained the largest in the world for 30 years. Then came the great jump from 100 to 200 inches, the result of the imagination and leadership of the late G. E. Hale. He had been concerned with the building first of the Yerkes refractor, and then with the Mount Wilson reflector, but still looked further. The great problem was to obtain a suitable disk for the mirror, and several years of disappointment preceded the successful casting at the end of 1934 (6). The site chosen was Mount Palomar (5,600 feet) in California and in 1948 the telescope was ready for

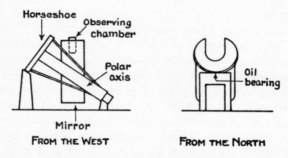

Fig. 19. Mounting the 200 inch telescope

testing and adjustment (7). The mirror has a focal length of just over 50 feet, but as in the case of the Radcliffe instrument the effective focal length can be greatly increased by using the Cassegrain and Coudé systems. The unusual feature is the method of mounting, Fig. 19. Radcliffe is supported from one side only; Mt. Wilson from both sides, but in such a way that the view of the polar regions is obstructed. The remarkable U-shaped bearing at the north end permits this telescope to be directed at the pole itself if desired; the total weight of the moving parts is 450 tons, but by forcing oil under the bearing with high pressure very free frictionless movement is obtained. At the focus of the mirror and visible in

Plate II (p. 57) there is a chamber in which the observer actually works! The history of this telescope is a remarkable and human story of success over many difficulties (8). The study of stellar spectra and the external galaxies (Chs. VI and VII) are expected to be the main fields of research to which it will be devoted.

What of telescopes in Great Britain? At the Greenwich Observatory, in addition to the 28 and 26 inch refractors, and the instruments needed for the positional astronomy for which the Observatory was founded, there are 30 and 36 inch reflectors, built in 1897 and 1934 respectively. There are also 36 inch reflectors at Edinburgh and Cambridge. Conditions at Greenwich have gradually deteriorated, industrial and domestic smoke in the air, and artificial lighting, particularly of the modern mercury vapour type, have made much desirable observational work impossible, and the sulphur-polluted atmosphere causes rapid tarnishing of the mirrors. Shortly after the war it was announced that the castle and park at Herstmonceux had been acquired as a site for a new Royal Greenwich Observatory. To this spot near the Sussex coast, where the weather and atmosphere are as good as could be found in these islands, our national observatory is gradually moving from its famous home near the Thames. Why no big telescope? The usual explanation is that the weather is so bad that it would be a waste of money to build one—but is it? Early in 1946 Prof. H. H. Plaskett, in his Presidential address to the Royal Astronomical Society, made a strong plea for a large telescope in this country. As a result of this a committee of that body prepared a case to put before the Royal Society, and remarkably interesting it is (9). They proposed that a 72 inch reflector be erected at Herstmonceux and named in honour of Newton, the maker of the first reflector. A few points made were that without a large telescope Britain's contribution to astronomy would dwindle away, the quality of the seeing here was as good as in most places, that in spite of our famous weather the number of clear hours at Herstmonceux was estimated to be more than in Western Canada where the Victoria 72 inch had been doing excellent work for years, and if there are limited opportunities of seeing the sky we must have a really good telescope to make the most of them. The upshot was that on the opening day of the Newton Tercentenary Celebrations, the President of the Royal Society announced that the Chancellor of the Exchequer had agreed to ask Parliament to vote a sum of money to build the Isaac Newton Observatory, equipped with a 100 inch telescope. It is very tempting to consider these proposals in more detail, but this chapter is keeping us earth-bound quite long enough as it is and readers who are interested must look eleswhere (10), (11). It is very gratifying to know that the country where so much was done in the nineteenth century is not, after all, to be left behind in the twentieth.

Photography

This will be a comparatively short section, and its shortness must not lead to an underestimate of the value of photography in astronomy. References to photography will occur naturally in other parts of the book; a few general ideas only will be given here. One great advantage is that it records a whole situation at one time, an advantage that has been widely used in preparing maps of star fields. Without the camera the position of each star must be found separately with the telescope; the camera records the whole field and the resulting plate can be examined at leisure. Such plates are regularly used for the detection of relative motions among the stars, and without the photographic method our knowledge of parallax and proper motion would be severely limited.

When starlight falls on the eye it stimulates the nerves within the eye and we see the star—if sufficient energy has been received. If the star is too faint to see, it is no use continuing to gaze at the spot. The effect of a telescope, as has been explained, is to collect more light as in a funnel and pour it into the eye, thus making brighter and visible the star that could not be seen. The effect of light on a photographic plate is cumulative. If there is not enough light to make the necessary chemical change in the plate in one minute, then use a hundred, or in fact as many as necessary. With long exposures the camera reveals things that the eye has never seen. The cumulative effect has a disadvantage too. Owing to the earth's atmosphere the quality of the seeing varies from moment to moment, and the photograph is an average view in which detail, only momentarily visible, has been obliterated. An observer may see these fleeting details and thus in his drawing record something that the camera cannot. The camera has not rendered obsolete the man at the telescope, there is still a need for both.* A long time exposure will demand that the photographic apparatus be fitted on an equatorial mounting, and if the speed of rotation of the polar axis is in exact agreement with that of the earth the star images will be small disks and any rapidly moving object, e.g. a minor planet, will trail. This is the method of searching for quick moving objects; where the motion is too slow to trail during the appropriate

*Compare the two pictures of Jupiter in Plate VI, p. 113.

E

time exposure the object can be detected by comparing two separate photographs taken with a suitable time interval between them. If the object to be photographed has a rapid motion relative to the stars the rate of drive must be adjusted accordingly. Thus in comet photographs it is the stars that have trailed, well shown in Plate VII (p. 128).

A photograph of a star field may not look quite the same as the real thing, for stars vary a little in colour, and the photographic plate does not react to colour in the same way as the eye. If red, yellow and blue lights were photographed on 'ordinary' plates the blue would have most effect and the red none at all—in fact red is used for lighting the dark room during development. To the eye these three might look equally bright, but in the photograph widely different. This is an extreme case, for there are different kinds of photographic material and stars do not contrast as vividly as traffic lights. Nevertheless it is safe to say that the relative brightness of a group of stars will differ according to the method, photographic or visual, used to record them. In the constellation of Orion the bright star alpha, Betelgeuse, is hardly noticeable in a photograph, for it is a reddish star.

Celestial photographs fall into two main groups which we can conveniently call short focus and long focus. The former are taken with a camera not very different from those with which we are familiar, and the distance from lens to plate is short. This distance, the focal length, varies widely from one astronomical camera to another, and just to convey a rough idea it might be quoted as about two feet. This kind of camera gives a wide field and small scale and is used for such objects as a portion of the Milky Way. For the long focus photographs the

telescope itself forms the camera and the focal length may
be 100 feet or even more. These photographs are of a
small field on a large scale, such as a planet or a portion
of the moon. The two comet photographs on Plate VII
(p. 128) are of interest in this connection. The upper one
was taken with a telescope of about 12 feet focal length,
and shows a field 1° square. The lower one of the same
comet was done with a camera of 11 inches focal length,
and the picture is about 10° square. We will now leave
the subject of photography to 'turn up' where it will.

The Spectroscope

The writer remembers hearing a Professor of physics
say (in effect) 'I wish the schools would do more astronomy and teach their pupils to think; the laboratory
scientist can handle his material and control its conditions,
while the astronomer can only look at his from afar.' The
star is minute, a pin-point of light, yet the astronomer
can look at it with a suitable instrument and say 'that
star contains a lot of . . .; its temperature is about . . .; it is
moving away from us with a velocity of . . .;' and many
other things can be deduced from it too.

How is this miracle brought about? The dispersion of
light into its constituent colours is a familiar phenomenon,
seen in the bevelled edge of a mirror or in a drop of water
hanging from the tap. A common way of bringing it about
deliberately is to use a triangular glass prism, whereby a
narrow beam of white light is dispersed into the rainbow
colours called the spectrum, Fig. 20. A more elaborate arrangement used in laboratories is shown in Fig. 21. If there
were no prism and the telescope were in line with the
collimator one clear image of the narrow slit would be
seen; if the prism is present, as shown, and a neon shop

sign used to illuminate the slit there would be a number
of images of the slit, all in different colours. Light, like
sound, is a form of wave motion, and we must pause for
a moment to consider what that means.

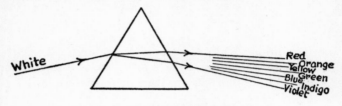

Fig. 20.   Dispersion of light by a prism

Watch a wave on the surface of the sea; the crest rolls
past, followed by a trough, but the water itself merely
moves up and down, as can be seen by watching the

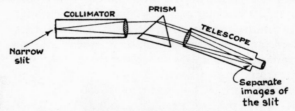

Fig. 21.   One arrangement for viewing spectra

floating seagulls. The motion of the water follows mathematical rules characteristic of wave motion. Consider
the transmission of sound through air. The air itself just
bobs to and fro through quite a small distance, causing
the pressure to vary in a rhythmic way similar mathematically to the variations in the height of the water. This
is a sound wave. When light passes through space there
are electric and magnetic variations going on, and as
these variations obey the wave motion rules, light is said

to consist of electromagnetic waves. Wireless waves and X-rays are also electromagnetic, and although we call these phenomena 'waves' there is nothing bobbing up and down like the seagulls. Imagine that these various waves could suddenly be halted, just as they are, for examination, and you could run your finger along the water wave. Start from a crest, run down into a hollow and up to a crest again; this is one wave length, Fig. 22 A.

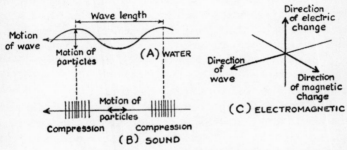

Fig. 22. Illustrating the nature of waves

In sound, B, one wave length is from a compression to the next compression. In both cases, and in electromagnetic waves too, the wavelength is the distance you would have to move to find the same conditions repeated. The frequency is the number of waves produced in unit time, and since the velocity is constant an increase in the length of the waves means proportionally fewer of them. This can be seen in the *Radio Times*, where each station is given its wavelength in metres and frequency in kilocycles; double one—halve the other.

Each key on a piano emits sound of a definite wavelength, an average wavelength near the middle of the keyboard being about two yards. A chord is a sound made up of several wavelengths together, and a musician can tell by ear what notes the chord contains. A neon lamp emits light of several definite wavelengths, this time of the order of a thousandth of a millimetre, but the eye cannot tell what they are. The spectroscope in Fig. 21 sorts them out by turning each through a different angle. If salt be put into a gas flame it gives an intense yellow, and when this is viewed with the spectroscope there is just a yellow line (really a close pair), corresponding to one note in sound. Every element has a group of wavelengths associated with it; analyse the light, measure its wavelengths, and the elements causing it are identified. White light contains all the wavelengths to which the eye is sensitive, and so in the spectroscope there is the familiar unbroken band of colour, the continuous spectrum.

The bright line spectrum, like the sodium flame and the neon lamp, is produced by elements in the form of a gas or vapour. Incandescent solids, such as an arc or filament lamp, give a continuous spectrum. Now if a sodium flame be placed between the lamp and the spectroscope the continuous band of light is found to be crossed by a dark line (or close pair) in the yellow, Fig. 23:2. This is due to the absorption by the sodium vapour of light of a particular wavelength. If now the lamp be turned off but the flame left burning, the bright background vanishes and exactly where the dark line was the bright yellow line appears, Fig. 23:1. Thus the wavelength absorbed by sodium is the same as that which it emits. The spectrum of sunlight is crossed by many of these absorption lines, called Fraunhofer's lines, and a few of these are shown in Fig. 23:3. Their wavelengths can be measured, and those of the pair marked D are the sodium wavelengths, said to be 5890 and 5896 angstrom units, one such unit being 10^{-8} or 0.00000001 cm. Therefore there must be sodium in the sun, though exactly where in the sun we can defer for the moment. Lines C and F have the wavelengths of hydrogen; hence there is hydrogen in the sun. Thus the spectroscope can tell us something about the composition of the sun, and of the stars, for they also show Fraunhofer's lines. The spectroscope can be arranged so that a spectrum from a laboratory

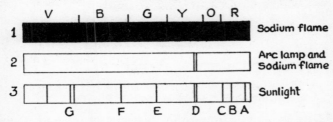

Fig. 23. Spectra: 1. Sodium flame; 2. Sodium flame in front of arc lamp; 3. Sunlight

source, like Fig. 23:1, can be viewed at the same time as and alongside the spectrum of the star. Lines can then be identified without the necessity of measuring the wavelengths.

The design of astronomical spectroscopes varies very widely according to the special purpose for which they are to be used, but details are not necessary in this book. Many of them use more than one prism to increase the dispersion and some work on a different principle, that of the diffraction grating. One variation must be mentioned, the spectrograph; here the spectrum, and the comparison spectrum, if any, is photographed. The photographic spectrum is not quite the same as the visual one. The wavelength of visible light is shortest at the violet end;

if it is any shorter than this it ceases to be visible and is called the ultra-violet radiation. It does, however, affect the photographic plate, and most photographs of spectra are about half in the ultra-violet region. There is also an infra-red region at the other end of the spectrum, and for some purposes in astronomy infra-red plates are used.

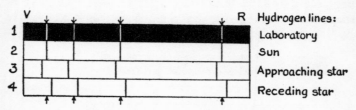

Fig. 24. Hydrogen lines in: 1. the laboratory; 2. the sun; 3. an approaching star; 4. a receding star

There is another important message of starlight to be obtained from the spectroscope, but again we must begin with the analogy of sound. The pitch of a note depends upon the frequency of the vibrations, a high note being due to a high frequency and short wavelength. If the source of sound is moving towards or away from the observer the pitch heard is not the true one, and everyone is familiar with the change in note as the source passes by, a common example being the sound of an aeroplane flying over the house. This phenomenon illustrates Doppler's principle and has its counterpart in light. When the source of sound is approaching, each wave has a shorter distance to travel than the previous one, and therefore arrives a little too soon. Thus in a given time, say one second, more waves arrive than would be the case with a stationary source. This means that an approaching source gives a higher frequency and shorter wavelength; similarly a receding source gives a lower frequency and longer wavelength. It has been pointed out that the lines in the spectrum of a star can be identified by use of a comparison spectrum. Sometimes the lines agree in spacing and arrangement with the comparison lines, but the whole lot have been shifted a little, Fig. 24. A displacement towards the violet means a shorter wavelength and an approaching star; displacement towards the red for a receding star. By measuring the Doppler shift the velocity of the star in the line of sight can be calculated.

The Spectrohelioscope

This is a special application of the spectroscope, largely developed by Hale and used for the examination of the sun (12). Refer to Fig. 21. Suppose that an image of the sun's disk be projected on to the slit; the means of doing so is normally the horizontal telescope illustrated in Fig. 17, the slit being placed in the focal plane of the main lens. The spectrum formed at the focus of the telescope lens consists of a series of images of the slit in all the colours that are present, in this case a continuous spectrum crossed by Fraunhofer's lines. Now let a second slit be placed across this spectrum; it will let through one only of these images and will therefore show to the eye a narrow strip of the sun in one colour only. If the chosen wavelength (colour) is that of the C line, due to hydrogen, the observer will see the distribution of this element in the strip of the sun concerned. By moving the sun's image right across the first slit, the second slit will show the hydrogen distribution over the whole of it, made up, of course, of an infinite number of narrow strips exhibited in succession. In practice it is not convenient to move the image, so the slits move, the first across the image and the second keeping pace with the C line as it travels across the focal plane of the telescope lens.

The way in which this is brought about is shown in Fig. 25. Mention has already been made of an alternative method of obtaining a spectrum, the diffraction grating, and this is used here. The grating is a piece of glass on which have been ruled, over an area about 3 inches square,

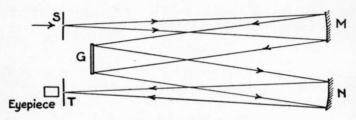

Fig. 25. The spectrohelioscope

a very large number of fine lines parallel with the slit. S is the first vertical slit, on which the sun's image falls. It is at the focus of the concave mirror M, which has a focal length of about 10 feet; light is reflected from this mirror as a parallel beam and falls on the grating G. This forms a spectrum, light of each colour reflecting off at a different angle. N is a similar mirror and it focuses the spectrum on the second slit T. The apparatus is actually arranged so that the second slit is vertically below the first (the diagram is a plan), just sufficiently below for the incident sunlight to pass over the observer's head. In a spectro-heliograph a photographic plate is placed immediately behind T, and with this arrangement the sun can be photographed in light of one colour; such a photograph is reproduced in Plate IX (p. 144). The slits of the spectrohelioscope, which move in opposite directions, must work sufficiently rapidly to utilise the phenomenon of persistence of vision. As is well known a cinema film consists of a series of still pictures, and when these are projected at a rate of not less than 16 a second the eye is unconscious of the change-over and a continuous moving picture is the result. Similarly with the instrument under discussion; if the slits are driven fast enough the observer sees the whole disk at once. The rapid drive introduces mechanical difficulties, and in many instruments the slits are kept at rest and the images of the sun and spectrum displaced by rotating a small square glass prism in front of each. Such an instrument has recently been built at Cambridge, and as it is intended to adapt it for taking photographs in ultra-violet light the main lens of the horizontal telescope has been replaced by another concave mirror. This is because ultra-violet radiation is seriously absorbed when passed through glass but not when reflected from a mirror. Arrangements are also being made at this observatory for examination of the sun in infra-red radiation.

The Photometer

Mention has been made in earlier chapters of the division of the stars into their magnitudes, the first 20 being classed as first, the next 50 or so as second, and so on. The scientific basis of this system must now be explained. The light ratio of 2.512 between one magnitude and the next gives an allocation of magnitudes not differing much from that handed down from ancient times, and this number has been adopted. Starting from a star of the second magnitude (about the brightness of the Pole Star), a first magnitude star will be 2.51 times as bright and a third would give $\frac{1}{2.51}$ of the light. The light ratio between the first and the third would be 2.51×2.51 or 2.51^2. A difference of five magnitudes corresponds to a light ratio of just 100. An instrument for comparing the intensities of the light from two stars is called a photometer, and if the magnitude of one star is known, that of the other can be calculated. The result is not necessarily a whole number; the Pole Star, for instance, is not exactly 2.0 but 2.1. The so-called first magnitude stars differ quite widely among themselves. To be of magnitude 1.0 the star must be 2.51 times brighter than a second, but what if it is 10 times? A difference of two magnitudes means a light ratio of 2.51^2, or 6.29. A difference of three gives 2.51^3 or 15.8. Thus a ratio of 10 means that the star is more than two magnitudes but less than three brighter than the second, actually 2.5. If this difference be subtracted from the original 2.0 we get -0.5; thus very bright stars have negative magnitudes.

The magnitude of an object is determined by comparing it with others to which a number has already been assigned, and there are various ways of making the comparison. The amateur observer of variable stars frequently does it by eye. He looks at the variable and at its neighbours, usually with his telescope, and finds that the variable is brighter than one and fainter than another. Thus he is able to fix its brightness to within about a tenth of a magnitude. Another method is to use a photometer which enables the stars to be matched in turn against an artificial star, which is, of course, a light in the observatory, but by far the most widespread way is photographic. Readers should remember that photographic methods will not give quite the same results as visual.

When a field of stars is photographed and the plate developed each star image appears as a little black spot of reduced silver. The size and density of the spot depends upon the brightness of the star (we are ignoring its colour), the length of exposure, the quality of the plate, and the state of the atmosphere. If, however, some of the stars in the field are of known magnitude, the others can be determined by comparing either the sizes or the densities of the spots, for the other factors will be constant for all the images on the plate. If the required comparison stars are not in the same field they must be photographed on the same plate as soon as possible after the first exposure, and the work must be done at a time when the stars on test are about the same altitude above the horizon as the comparison stars that it is desired to use. Modern apparatus for comparing the densities of star images make use of the photocell, which many readers will have heard of in connection with the sound cinema projector. It consists of an evacuated glass bulb containing a coating of a certain metal, caesium being commonly used, with a metal plate near to it. When light falls on the coating electrons, which are units of negative electricity, are expelled from it, the number depending on the quantity of light energy received. These fall upon the neighbouring plate and give rise to a small electric current. In the cinema the sound track is a narrow band of varying density on one edge of the film, and a small lamp shines through it on to the photocell. As the density changes so does the current; this is amplified like a radio signal, fed to a loud speaker, and out comes the sound. In the astronomical case a small light shines through a star image on to a photocell and the resulting current is recorded by a galvanometer. Needless to say, to convert galvanometer readings into star magnitudes requires an accurate knowledge of the behaviour of both the photocell and the original photographic plate. The accuracy is to about $\frac{1}{100}$ of a magnitude.

A technique is being developed by which the photocell is attached to the telescope and is operated by direct starlight. As the starlight is very feeble a special type of cell is used. This, within itself, amplifies the electric effect by a factor as big as a million; even so the current is very small, being of the order of a thousand millionth part of an ampere. Obviously a difficult measurement, so apparatus has been devised which will count the emitted electrons, and these counts are proportional to the radiation received.

For positional astronomy the observatory clock is an important instrument, but this topic is a study in itself and cannot be dealt with here. For those who are interested three references are given. The first (13) is about clocks in general, the second (14) describes the free pendulum clocks often used in observatories, and the last (15) is a brief account of the new quartz crystal clock.

Two more of the astronomer's weapons can be mentioned only. The first is mathematics, and although there is next to none in this book it should be obvious to the reader, from nearly every chapter, that without mathematics little progress would be made. Observations could be taken but not adequately interpreted; it is one of the most powerful weapons in the armoury. Lastly, radio. This is new to the astronomer and has been developed mainly since the war. During the Festival of Britain visitors to the South Bank Exhibition were able to hear the sun as well as see it—though not both at once, as the apparatus was inside the Dome of Discovery. This application is actually used in solar research, and radar methods have proved very useful for the detection of daylight meteors; both will be referred to again in the appropriate places. An astronomers' receiving aerial is illustrated in Plate III (p. 96).

REFERENCES

(1) See H. Knox-Shaw, *Occasional Notes of the R.A.S.*, I/45, 1939.

(2) Also a popular account of the installing of the mirror, by D. S. Evans, *Discovery*, IX/251, 1948.

(3) A popular account of the Schmidt camera is given by D. S. Evans, *Discovery*, X/314, 1949.

(4) A technical account by E. H. Linfoot, *Monthly Notices of the R.A.S.*, 108/81, 1948.

(5) An intermediate account by G. F. West, *School Science Review*, No. 113, 1949.

(6) A brief contemporary account of the project was given by G. E. Hale in *Nature*, 137/221, 1936.

(7) Illustrated description by M. Davidson, *Discovery*, IX/180, 1948.

(8) D. O. Woodbury, *The Glass Giant of Palomar*, 1948.

(9) *Monthly Notices of the R.A.S.*, 107/11, 1947.

(10) H. H. Plaskett, in *Discovery*, VII/311, 1946.

(11) D. H. Sadler, in *The Observatory*, 66/380, 1946.

(12) G. E. Hale, *Signals from the Stars*, 1932.

(13) D. de Carle, *British Time*, 1947.

(14) F. Hope-Jones, *Electrical Timekeeping*, 1940.

(15) M. W. Ovenden, 'The Quartz Clock'; *Journal of the B.A.A.*, 60/31, 1949.

CHAPTER IV

The Earth and its Satellite

The Earth

A VOLUME in this series is being devoted to the earth (1), so it need not be treated at any length in this one. Some consideration must be given, however, to the earth as a body in space. We know that it is approximately spherical in shape, though slightly shorter from pole to pole than across the equator. It floats in space supported on nothing, and any object in its neighbourhood falls, not down, but towards the earth's centre. Astronomers should not use such expressions as up and down or top and bottom.

The earth is rotating upon its shortest diameter, the axis, one end of which is called north and the other south. This axis, then, is one fundamental direction in space—the astronomer does use the expressions north and south. If the earth were viewed from above the north pole the rotation would appear anti-clockwise; many astronomical diagrams are drawn in this sense, and this rotation is said to be direct. We also know that this rotation from west to east causes the heavenly bodies to move across our sky from east to west. A rotation through 360°, which would bring a star from the meridian to the meridian again, is called a sidereal day and is a fundamental unit of time. In the last chapter, mention was made of the use of a transit instrument to check the accuracy of the clock against this fundamental unit. It is interesting to note that modern time-keeping devices are so regular that they can be used to check small irregularities in the spin of the earth! In connection with the transit instrument mention was made of the measurement of right ascension and declination, the co-ordinates by which the position of a star is fixed. The sky *looks* like a sphere seen from the inside; this is called the celestial sphere and its surface is mapped on globes and charts. The prolongation of the earth's axis meets this imaginary sphere in the celestial poles, and the plane of the earth's equator, perpendicular to the axis, meets the sphere in a line called the celestial equator. This, then, is one fundamental plane in space, for it is with reference to the plane of the equator that star maps are made. The maps at the end of this book have the celestial poles in the centre, and the celestial equator is one of the circles there shown.

Another well-known fact is that the earth is revolving around the sun once a year. Its path or orbit is an ellipse, and the motion is direct, i.e. if seen from a distant point over the north pole the earth would be moving anti-clockwise around the sun. Unfortunately we cannot suspend ourselves in that position (yet!) but we can infer that motion from the fact that the sun has an annual direct west to east motion among the background of stars; evidence for this motion was considered in Ch. II. Its path among the stars is called the ecliptic and passes through the twelve constellations known as the Signs of the Zodiac. When you draw a diagram, showing the sun, the earth and the earth's orbit, the orbit will be in the plane of the paper. Similarly the real orbit lies in a plane, and this plane if extended to meet the star sphere does so in the line called the ecliptic. This 'plane of the ecliptic' is the second fundamental plane in space, and is used in

F

problems concerning the solar system. When we come
to deal with the distribution of the stars even this will not
do; we shall use the plane of the Milky Way. The intersection of these two planes with the celestial sphere are
also shown on the map.

We now come to the relationship between our two
planes; they are inclined at an angle of $23\frac{1}{2}°$. They

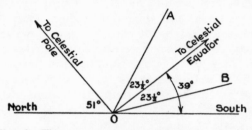

Fig. 26.   The seasonal change in the altitude of the sun

intersect in a line which cuts the star sphere in two points
called the equinoxes and which can be seen on the end
map where the circles representing the equator and ecliptic meet. These two points are known also as the First
Point of Aries, where in March the sun moves north of
the equator, and the First Point of Libra where in September it moves south. The reason why these points are
not situated in the constellations of Aries and Libra must
be deferred for a few moments. The subject of seasons is
dealt with adequately in the geography books and is
illustrated in most atlases, so it can be passed over quickly
now. The reason is the earth's tilt, which means that its
axis of rotation is not perpendicular to the plane of the
ecliptic, but is tilted through $23\frac{1}{2}°$. Let us consider one
or two other features of this 'obliquity of the ecliptic'.

In Fig. 26 the plane of the paper is the meridian and

the observer is at o. Assuming that the observer is in latitude 51° the altitude of the celestial pole is also 51° and that of the equator must be 39°. When the sun is at either equinox its meridian altitude, at midday, must be 39°. In June it is between Taurus and Gemini (see map), where the ecliptic is at its maximum distance north of the equator. The sun therefore appears in direction OA

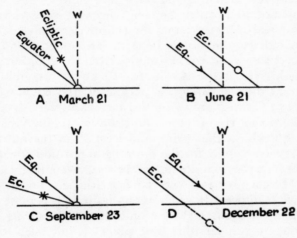

Fig. 27. The seasonal change in the setting of the sun

at an altitude of 62½°. It follows that in December, when in the constellation of Scorpio, it will be seen in direction OB. Thus there is a wide variation, in our latitude, in the altitude of the sun.

Fig. 27 shows the aspect due west at 6.0 p.m. on four significant dates for an observer in the latitude of England. In each the ecliptic, equator and the sun are depicted, and an arrow to show the apparent motion. It is obvious that on two of these dates the sun is just setting. In June not only has the sun not set, but when it does it will be tó the north of west; in December it has already set, and south of west at that. Thus we see why the length of the day varies, for similar conditions apply when rising in the east.

Consider a planet; its motion is always quite close to the ecliptic. When in the same line as the sun it is in conjunction and cannot be seen, and as it emerges as an evening star it moves along the ecliptic, until at last it is far enough from the sun to be seen. In Fig. 27 A and C a planet is shown, at equal distance from the sun, but how much higher in the sky in A. Remembering that the apparent diurnal motion is parallel to the equator, the planet at C is not only very low but it will very soon set. Thus a planet rises from conjunction to evening visibility most quickly in the spring and least so in the autumn. The reverse applies for the morning apparition when the planet is on the opposite side of the sun. We already know that Mercury is never very far from the sun and is consequently difficult to see. In our latitude it is most easy to find if the evening elongation occurs in the spring, and without instruments this little planet is not likely to be seen at all if elongation occurs in the autumn.

The moon moves along the ecliptic (or rather quite close to it) quite rapidly, and thus the daily change in its altitude at 6.0, or in its time of setting, is greatest in March, and least in September. The full moon rises at 6.0 p.m. and the same rules apply. Thus the full moon near the end of the latter month rises as the sun goes down, and for several days in succession the time of moonrise gets later by only a few minutes a day. This is the 'harvest moon', enabling workers in the fields to go on late without having to do their task in the dark. The apparently large size of the harvest moon (2), (3), and of any other rising moon for that matter, is an optical illusion and need not be discussed here.

The earth's mean distance from the sun is 93,000,000 miles; the method by which this distance is found will be deferred until the next chapter. The orbit, however, is not a circle but an ellipse in accordance with Kepler's first law, and the distance therefore varies. When nearest to the sun early in January, in the position called perihelion, the earth is at a distance of about 91,400,000 miles, and in aphelion at the beginning of July about 94,600,000 miles. The difference is not large in proportion and the resultant change in apparent size of the sun is not noticeable though quite measurable. There is, however, another consequence which does become noticed.

The earth rotates on its axis in one sidereal day, and in that time a given point in the heavens will have rotated from the meridian westwards and back to the meridian again. If the sun should be at that point on the first day it will not be so on the second, for in the interval it will have moved about a degree eastwards along the ecliptic. Before the sun comes up to the meridian again the earth must turn through this degree, which takes about 4 minutes. Thus the solar day is 4 minutes longer than the sidereal, and as the sun, not the stars, rules man's activities we say that the length of the sidereal day is 23 h. 56 m. (and a few seconds that need not worry us here) in solar time. Now since the orbit of the earth is an ellipse and the Kepler's second law (see page 34) must be obeyed the orbital velocity of about 18½ miles per second is not uniform, and for this reason, coupled with the obliquity of the ecliptic, the motion of the sun among the stars is not constant either. This means that the extra bit that the earth must turn to bring the sun back to the meridian will vary from day to day—the solar day is not of uniform length.

The sundial records local solar time, and as long as this was the normal time-keeper the variations in the length of the day did not matter. The coming of mechanical clocks changed the situation, and we now use mean solar time for civil purposes. Thus in general the sundial and the time signals do not agree and the difference, called the equation of time, may be anything up to a quarter of an hour. The dial and the clock do agree, i.e. the equation of time is zero, on or about April 15, June 15, September 1 and December 25. The dial is fast by the clock between the first two dates, slow for the second interval, fast for the third, and slow again from December 25 to April 15. Readers who wish to check this should remember that the time signals give a standard time for an area, such as Greenwich Mean Time, not the local time for your town or village. The difference here depends upon the longitude of the observer (see geography books for the explanation) and may or may not have been allowed for when the dial was set. An old one such as may be found on a church wall is pretty sure to give local time, but a modern one may be giving Greenwich solar time. But how do the general public come to notice the equation of time? Let us take an example. About December 5 the day is exactly eight hours long, so according to the sundial the sun rises at 8.0 a.m. and sets at 4.0 p.m. But at this time of year the dial is ten minutes fast by the clock, so the clock—and hence the general public—finds sunrise to be at 7.50 and sunset at 3.50. The morning is therefore longer than the afternoon by 20 minutes. Mornings and afternoons usually do differ, but it seems to be only about Christmas time, when people are anxiously waiting for the dark days to lengthen, that the phenomenon is commented on by a puzzled public.

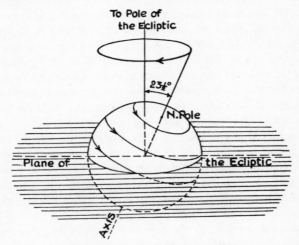

Fig. 28. The precession of the equinoxes

Now we must return to the problem of why the Signs of the Zodiac do not agree with the months to which they are assigned, why the First Point of Aries is not in Aries at all. Fig. 28 shows the plane of the ecliptic and the line perpendicular to it and through the earth's centre; this points to the pole of the ecliptic. The earth's axis makes an angle of 23½° with this line, and as it is spinning on its axis it maintains this angle just as a high speed top will do. Now this statement is not quite complete. Sometimes a top develops a slow wobble, the end of its axis tracing out a circle, and this is what is happening in the case of the earth. The reason cannot be explained in this book; it must suffice to say that it is due to the action of the sun and moon on a body which is not a perfect sphere. The effect is that the celestial pole is moving around the pole of the ecliptic in a period of 26,000 years. Thus the present Pole Star has not always been such; the pole is still getting nearer to it, and after about A.D. 2100 it will move away again. At the same time the First Point of Aries is moving westwards along the ecliptic at a rate of about 50 seconds of arc per annum. Many centuries ago, when the Zodiacal constellations were invented, this point, where the passing of the sun denotes the spring equinox, was in Aries and at one time in the distant past the pole was not far from the star α (alpha) Draconis. This equinoctial point is the zero for the measurement of right ascension and declination, so it follows that these measurements are slowly changing, as can be seen if you compare old star maps with new ones. The whole phenomenon is known as the 'precession of the equinoxes'.

We sometimes read the expression 'weighing the earth'. Expressed like this it is just nonsense; what is really meant is determining its mass, the quantity of matter composing it, in terms of some easily recognised quantity such as the gram, the pound or the ton. In his law of gravitation Newton stated that every massive body attracts every other, and this attractive force can be calculated from the formula $F = \dfrac{Gmm^1}{d^2}$ where m and m^1 are the masses concerned, d is the distance between their centres of gravity, and G is a universal constant. The value of G can be determined in the laboratory. It is an extremely small number, and so the force between manageable masses is also very small and difficult to measure. In the first attempt (Maskelyne, 1774) a mountain in Scotland was used as one of the masses, but with the refinement of more modern times spheres of lead and gold have proved adequate. Once G has been found we are able to attack the masses of many of the heavenly bodies. Let m^1 be the mass of some object on the earth's surface. Its value is known, and also its distance from the centre of the earth. When G is also known m can be calculated and this is the mass of the earth, which is about 6,000 million million million tons.* Knowing the mass of the earth it is then possible to find those of the moon and the sun.

Now a brief word about the atmosphere, brief because it has already received full treatment in this series (4). It is at once an astronomical nuisance and a biological necessity. On the one hand it obscures our view; it makes the stars twinkle; it displaces their images from their true positions; it gives the spells of bad seeing which ruin large scale photographs of planetary detail. Some people are looking forward to the time when they can get outside it in space ships and use their instruments from there. On the other hand, apart from the more obvious needs of living things it acts as a thermostat, preventing the temperature from rising very high or falling very low; it protects us from the harmful effects of excessive ultraviolet radiation from the sun and from the ceaseless bombardment of meteorites; it gives us the twilight and the blue sky. Enough said; we are indeed fortunate in our atmosphere and must make the best of its drawbacks.

The Moon

The earth is accompanied in its journey around the sun by an attendant body, or satellite, the moon. The

* 5.88×10^{21}.

orbit of the moon can be considered from two points of view, relative to the earth or relative to the sun. It appears to us to revolve around the earth at a mean distance of 239,000 miles, but if the apparent diameter of the moon be measured regularly throughout the month it is found to vary, showing that the orbit, like that of the earth around the sun, is an ellipse. The distance of the moon can be determined by a trigonometrical method

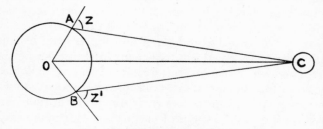

Fig. 29. Finding the distance of the moon

similar to that used in surveying the earth's surface. A point C is observed from points A and B and its directions noted. Then if the distance AB is known the triangle ABC can be solved. In Fig. 29 A and B are two observatories a long way apart and for simplicity assumed to be on the same meridian. C is a point on the moon, and when this point is on the meridian its zenith distances Z and Z^1 are determined at the two observatories; this measurement is quite a straightforward matter. From the zenith distances the angles OAC, OBC can be found; AOB is the known difference in latitude between the two observatories; OA and OB are known; thus it is possible to calculate all the other lines in the diagram. The moon's orbit does not differ very widely from a circle. Its distance is approximately 222,000 miles when at its nearest point, perigee, and 253,000 at the furthest, apogee. Its apparent angular diameter varies from about 29½ minutes of arc to 33. Note that this diameter is about half a degree; an angle through which the earth rotates in two minutes. Thus while you are watching the moon through a telescope it seems to cross its own diameter in only two minutes. Knowing the distance and angular diameter of

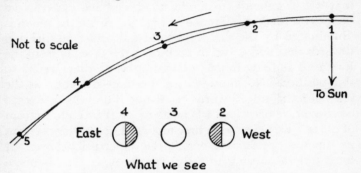

Fig. 30. The moon's path relative to the sun

the moon it is a simple task to deduce its actual diameter, which is 2160 miles, or just over a quarter of that of the earth.

If we regard the sun, instead of the earth, as the fixed point of reference, the moon's orbit is almost the same as the earth's, for the radius of this orbit is 93 million miles and the distance of the moon from it is never more than a quarter of a million. The path of the moon, however, is interlacing that of the earth in the way shown in Fig. 30, which is not to scale. An important point to note is that it is always concave towards the sun.

The moon, like the earth, is a solid body and is not self

luminous, it shines like many other things with reflected sunlight. Only one half of its globe is illuminated and we may see only a part of that half; this accounts for the phases or changing apparent shape of our satellite. It should not be necessary here to make an exhaustive explanation of this phenomenon. Most good atlases include an explanatory diagram based on the orbit of the moon relative to the earth. There are, however, a few points that are frequently misunderstood and we can discuss them with further reference to Fig. 30. Since the moon is illuminated by the sun the bright half must be directed towards that body, and in position 1 this is away from the Earth. The 'new moon' quoted in your diary refers to this position. Not only is it in the same direction as the sun, but the side towards us is not illuminated; except on those rare occasions when the moon is actually in front of the sun we never see a new moon. The slender crescent in the west at sunset, which the superstitious must or must not (according to taste) see through glass is not a new moon but a young moon, or better still the 'waxing crescent'. As the days go by the crescent widens until position 2, when as the moon has made a quarter of a revolution it is in the position known as First Quarter, and we see a half moon facing west. No. 3 is full moon, 4 is third or Last Quarter, and 5 is new moon again. Between 4 and 5 we have the waning crescent or old moon in the east before sunrise, and all the way from 3 to 5 the illuminated part faces east. There seems to be a feeling that a crescent must be a new moon. When the *Queen Elizabeth* made her maiden voyage as a liner a press report stated that as she tied up at 7.39 a.m. 'The new moon disappeared behind a bank of cloud, but not before many people aboard had turned over their money for luck.'

Some people seem surprised to see the moon in daylight, but why not? At first quarter the angle between the sun and the moon is 90°, so if the sun is in the south, as at noon, the moon should be rising in the east and for the rest of the day will follow the sun, with its bright convex side facing west. The time of rising is, on an average, 50 minutes later each day, so the full moon rises at about 6.0 p.m. and is south at midnight. Last quarter will rise at about midnight, and, like the waning crescent, will still be visible during the morning daylight, facing east.

Some significance has been attached to 'the new moon on its back', meaning the horns or cusps pointing upwards. The direction of the sun is perpendicular to the line joining the horns, and as the moon lies close to the ecliptic on which the sun does lie, the line of the horns must be approximately at right angles to the ecliptic. If the situation were as shown in Fig. 27 A the crescent, though not quite on its back would be tilted well over, whereas in C it would be setting nearly upright.

Speaking of the horns brings to mind the lines:

> Till clomb above the eastern bar
> The horned Moon with one bright star
> Within the nether tip.

There cannot, of course be a star within the horns, for the rest of the moon is there, but such a scene has been reported in the past more than once (5). The star may have been close to the dark limb and its position misjudged, or it may not have been a star at all but a sunlit mountain top on the moon's surface. The rest of the moon can sometimes be seen dimly within the crescent, the 'old moon in the young moon's arms'. We all know how bright full moonlight can be; earthlight on the moon is many times brighter, and at the time when the moon to us is just past new, it is just past full earth over there. Thus we see the crescent in sunshine and the remainder of the disk in earthshine.

The time taken for the moon to go around the earth is $27\frac{1}{3}$ days, yet this is not what we understand by a month. Fig. 30 is drawn so that in 1 the line from the earth to the moon is pointing vertically down the page as well as towards the sun. When the moon has revolved through $360°$ in $27\frac{1}{3}$ days it will again be in this position and would be passing the same star in the sky, but the line down the page no longer points to the sun—the revolution must be continued for a little longer. The month measured from new moon to new moon, the duration of the cycle of phases, is $29\frac{1}{2}$ days.

The altitude of the moon when on the meridian, its highest point for the day, varies very widely. We have seen how in latitude $51°$, the altitude of the sun varies through $47°$, Fig. 26. The same would apply to the moon if it were truly in the ecliptic, and since the full moon and the sun are on opposite sides of the earth the high sun at midday in the summer would correspond with a low moon at midnight, and vice versa. But the plane of the moon's orbit is inclined at $5°$ with the plane of the ecliptic. If the most northerly point in the moon's orbit happened to coincide with the most northerly point in the ecliptic the maximum altitude of the moon would be $5°$ more than OA in Fig. 26; if the moon reached the northern point of the ecliptic (Taurus-Gemini) when at the southern limit of its own orbit its maximum altitude would be $5°$ less than OA. So which does it do? The answer to that is, both. The moon crosses the plane of the ecliptic in two points called its nodes, moving north of the plane at the ascending node and south again at the descending node, and

the line joining these nodes is not fixed in space. The
moon's nodes are moving in a retrograde (east-west)
direction along the ecliptic, and make a complete revolution in 18⅔ years.

So far nothing has been said about the rotation of the
moon upon its axis, which is another of the points of
misunderstanding. We see always the same side of the
moon; therefore it cannot be rotating—but to achieve this
result it both can and must rotate. Refer back to Fig. 30
and remember the experimental fact that the same face is
always directed towards the earth. In position 1 the
familiar 'man in the moon' has his face towards the top
of the page, in 2 to the left, in 3 to the bottom, in 4 to
the right. The moon does rotate on its axis in the same
period as it revolves about the earth, 27⅓ days. 'The man
in the moon' is the face that some see in the full moon,
though even to them it vanishes when a telescope is used.
It appears, then, that we see only one hemisphere and
until the rocket people can get to it man can never know
what is on the other side. As a matter of fact we do see a
little more. The orbit of the moon being an ellipse, the
speed with which the orbit is traversed is not constant, in
accordance with Kepler's second law. The speed of
rotation is constant. When the moon is moving fast near
perigee it gets a little ahead of station giving us a slight
peep around the western edge. Later it falls behind its
mean place and we see a little extra on the east limb.
This is called Libration in longitude, but there is a
latitude effect as well, for the moon's equator makes an
angle of 6½° with the ecliptic. Thus sometimes the axis is
tilted towards the earth and we see a little more of the
north polar regions, and when tilted away from us a little
extra in the south. The result of libration is that we are

able to see roughly 7° extra all around. At any instant the observer sees just under 50% of the moon's surface, but we are able to see 59% of it at one time or another.

Conditions on the Moon

When the moon is viewed with the naked eye the most obvious feature is the large dark areas. Before the days of telescopes these were thought to be seas, and were given fanciful names such as Sea of Tranquillity and Ocean of Storms. It did not seem to occur to the old astronomers that had they really been sheets of water there would occasionally be flashes of reflected sunlight. The smallest telescope shows their real nature, that the dark areas are comparatively level plains and that the light parts are mountains. These latter form in some cases ranges of mountains; they are named after their terrestrial counterparts, such as the Alps and the Apennines. Their commonest form, however, is in rings of many sizes, known collectively as craters from their resemblance to volcanoes, though they are, of course, very much larger. These are named after the ancient men of learning; Copernicus, Tycho and Kepler are there, together with a few more recent people such as Rosse and Lockyer. Plate IV (p. 97) is a photograph of the moon on which these three main types of object can be found in profusion. Before going on with a more detailed examination of the lunar surface we must pause for a while to consider the conditions under which they exist. The moon is a very different place from the earth, so it is not surprising that its surface, though it has its resemblances, differs so markedly from our own.

In its journey around the sky it is obvious that the moon must pass in front of the stars. The passage of the moon over a star is called an 'occultation', and these phenomena

III

16-24 inch Schmidt camera at Edinburgh Observatory

Cox, Hargreaves and Thomson

A radio telescope at Jodrell Bank, Cheshire

A. C. B. Lovell

IV

The moon aged 20 days
Lick Observatory Photograph

Limb visible
before full moon

Area of
Plate Va.

MARE FRIGORIS

Plato ○ Aristoteles

SINUS
IRIDUM

Pico ○ Eudoxus

Alps

Aristillus

Caucasus

Posidonius

MARE
CRISIUM

MARE IMBRIUM

Archimedes

Apennines

MARE
Linné

SERENITATIS

Aristarchus

Kepler

Eratosthenes

Copernicus

Hyginus

MARE
TRANQUILLITATIS

OCEANUS
PROCELLARUM

rimaldi

Ptolemaeus

Alphonsus

Theophilus

Cyrillus

Catharina

MARE
HUMORUM

MARE
NUBIUM

Str. Wall

Plate Vb

Tycho

KEY TO PLATE IV

A few of the objects named in this map and mentioned
in the text are hardly discernible in a small photograph

G

are accurately timed to provide data for checking the moon's motion. When the occultation is about to take place, say at a bright limb, our satellite moves nearer and nearer to the star, and the latter continues to shine with its normal brightness until it suddenly vanishes. Sometimes this last instant is difficult to see as the star may be confused with irregularities on the surface. In a dark limb occultation the star just goes out; it is there—it is not there—no warning. The easiest kind of occultation to watch is at the dark limb of an earthlit new moon. The significance of this at the moment is that the moon cannot have any appreciable atmosphere, for if it had the starlight would be dimmed before extinction and at the time of a solar eclipse (explanation to follow) the atmosphere would be visible as a bright rim around the moon's disk.

There are theoretical reasons for this lack of atmosphere; for the purpose of discussion let us consider that of the earth. All matter, solid, liquid and gas, is made up of small particles, called molecules, so small that they could be lined up millions to the inch. Now these molecules are always in motion; in the solid state their movement is somewhat restricted, but in gases they move quite freely. This free movement accounts for the ready expansion of a gas when put with a larger vessel, and for diffusion when gases are mixed. The molecules are not all moving at the same velocity, but from the kinetic theory of gases the average velocity of the molecules of a particular gas and at a particular temperature can be calculated. Thus the molecules of the gases forming the atmosphere tend to dissipate into space, and the lighter the gas the greater this tendency.

Now think of a projectile being discharged from the

earth's surface at a high velocity. The pull of gravity retards it and it gets slower and slower. But as it gets higher the retarding force gets weaker. Can gravity stop it before becoming too weak to do so; can the projectile maintain its velocity until gravity has become too weak? The initial velocity is the determining factor, and if the body were projected with a velocity of seven miles per second it would get away; the velocity of escape is seven miles per second. This, of course, is a problem for the inter-planetary travellers (6). A velocity like this cannot be created instantaneously, especially if human beings themselves were to acquire it; it would take time, and during this time a rocket using any fuel at present available would be burning it at a prodigious rate. The problem is not so much one of celestial navigation as one of finding a suitable propellant, one that will permit the space ship to carry sufficient of it to get out into space.

Returning to the atmosphere. Molecular velocities are high; the average for hydrogen at o°C, the freezing point of water, is just over one mile per second, and oxygen a quarter of that. At higher temperatures the velocity would be higher. These are average velocities and are well below the velocity of escape, but some of the molecules will be very much faster than the average and may be lost. It has been shown that an atmosphere will dissipate for average molecular velocities well below the velocity of escape—it would only be a matter of time, and, for a fraction of the escape velocity as low as one quarter the time would be astronomically short.* The moon is a smaller and very much less massive body than the earth, and its gravitational pull is therefore less. The velocity of escape is only 1½ miles per second, so it is not surprising

* Approx. 50,000 years.

that its atmosphere, if it ever had any, has been lost. Water is easily vaporised, especially under low pressure, so this has been lost too. Some authorities are not satisfied that every trace of air and water has gone from the moon and believe that there is some small remainder too tenuous for direct detection.

This lack of atmosphere will have far reaching effect on the land surface. On the earth the rocks are partly igneous, forced up from below in a molten state, and partly sedimentary laid down as deposits in water. The latter, upon which the terrestrial landscape so greatly depend, are necessarily absent from the moon; its surface is mainly volcanic. Then on our own globe the original rock formations are greatly changed, and in particular smoothed, by weathering. Wind, frost, rain, and above all running water, have shaped our land. This cannot happen on the moon; it retains its initial rugged grandeur. One form of denudation will go on, for the expansion and contraction of the rocks due to the unusually wide temperature range prevailing will in due course lead to fragmentation, with resulting scree-like slopes. Pictures of lunar landscapes frequently exaggerate the wildness and show the mountains excessively steep and tooth-like (7). Notice in Plate V (p. 112) the contrast between light and shadow; where the sun's rays fall directly it is light, where they do not is darkness. There is no general diffused light as we have here, and there will be a black sky, from which the stars shine steadily day and night, though not easy to see in daylight owing to the eye being dazzled by the brilliant landscape. There will also be a coldness about the illumination of the moon, for the shorter wave-lengths in the incident light, which with an atmosphere would have given a blue sky, come right through unimpeded. Some of this radiation is in the extreme ultra-violet region and is harmful to life.

The day on the moon is equal to 14 of ours, and during this time the sun beats down relentlessly in all its power. There is reason to believe that a large part of the lunar surface, such as the great plains, is composed mainly of volcanic ash, .which is a very bad conductor of heat. Thus the surface temperature must be high. The radiant heat from the moon has been measured and corresponds to a surface temperature of 125°C, hotter than boiling water. Then follows the long night, with no atmospheric blanket to keep the heat in. Everyone knows that in our own country a clear sky on a winter night foretells frost before morning. The moon has the clear sky, and how clear, every night, and the temperature is likely to fall to −100°C. In our domestic Fahrenheit scale this means a temperature range from 180 degrees of frost to 45 degrees above boiling point; what an inhospitable place!

The astronomical telescope gives an inverted image. It is therefore usual for pictures and maps of the moon to be reproduced upside down; Plate IV (page 97) and its key are upright views, as seen with ordinary binoculars. It will at once be noticed that the dark areas, the 'seas' or maria, are mainly located in the upper, or, northern hemisphere. They vary in size, and their margins are in general quite clearly bounded by mountain barriers, though they do communicate with one another in places. Mare Crisium (Sea of Crises) is small and particularly well bounded; its longest dimension is 350 miles. Mare Imbrium (Sea of Showers) is the greatest of these features, with a length of 750 miles and breadth 670 miles. Its boundaries are very fine, with the mountain range of the Apennines to the south and the beautiful Sinus Iridum (Gulf of Rainbows) on the north. As the photographs show the surfaces of the maria are not really smooth but are dotted with ridges and hollows.

The appearance of the so-called craters varies considerably with the direction of illumination. Compare Kepler or Copernicus, which when Plate IV was taken were illuminated with a high sun of some 50-70° altitude, with Theophilus, where the sun was very low to the left of the picture and cast deep shadows to the right of every eminence. Compare also the sunset photograph in Plate V (p. 112) with the corresponding area in Plate IV, where the altitude of the sun was higher. The rings really fall into several classes, large ring plains with a flat floor, large with a central mountain, and smaller and more genuine craters. Archimedes is a good example of the first type; it is 50 miles in diameter but the mountain ramparts are comparatively low at 4,000 feet. The heights of lunar mountains above neighbouring level ground can be deduced from the length of the shadow when the angle of the sun's rays is known. Plato is a much studied object, similar but slightly larger and higher. The ring includes several well marked peaks and the floor, darker than most of the lunar surface, contains many small objects difficult to see and of constant interest to enthusiasts. Two outstanding examples of the second group are Tycho and Copernicus, though Theophilus also shows up well in the photograph. Tycho and Copernicus are both between 50 and 60 miles in diameter, with their mountain walls some 12,000 feet above the interior. The walls show terraces, and in each case the central mountain is a group of peaks rather than one. Theophilus is of similar size, but with ramparts rising to a maximum of 18,000 feet. These heights are from the interiors; there is no 'mean sea level' on the moon. A few of the flat floor type, such as Alphonsus, look as though there had been central mountains in the past and only its debris remain. The third group calls for no comment. They can be found in the photographs in large numbers, some appearing like miniature reproductions of their big brothers and others little more than hollows in the maria.

Of the mountain ranges the most striking, in the writer's opinion, is the Apennines, some 400 miles long, with Mount Wolf (12,000 feet) at the S.E. end, Mount Hadley (15,000 feet) at the other, and Mounts Bradley and Huyghens (16,000-20,000 feet) between.

There are also numerous lesser objects of much interest. Valleys and clefts explain themselves, the latter being of the nature of cracks in a comparatively smooth surface. The greatest valley cuts right through the mountain mass of the Alps, and is 83 miles long and about 5 miles wide. A famous cleft is that associated with the small crater Hyginus near the centre of the disk. Isolated mountains also occur, Mount Pico (8,000 feet), not far from Plato, being a notable example. Another interesting object is the Straight Wall, situated in Mare Nubium (Sea of Clouds) and looking like a straight ridge 65 miles long and 500 feet high. It is really a cliff caused by a great fault in the rocks, against which the adjacent land has subsided. Finally we come to the mysterious rays radiating around certain of the craters under high illumination, notably Tycho, Copernicus and Kepler. Their nature is a mystery, as they go on for many miles over hill and plain and cast no shadow. Kepler is famous on account of its extreme brightness, though the neighbouring Aristarchus is probably brighter still.

The question is sometimes raised whether any volcanic

activity still goes on in this volcanic land, and in general terms the answer is no. There is one object, the crater Linné in Mare Serenitatis (Sea of Serenity), in which some change *may* have occurred. It was originally recorded as a deep crater, but sometime in the sixties of the last century it was seen to resemble 'a whitish cloud surrounding a small elliptic crater'. This suggests that some lava outflow may have filled up the former deep crater, but the whole situation is in some doubt, and although the crater was carefully watched for many years nothing seems to have happened since.

Apart from the beautiful photographs made with great telescopes this science of selenography is largely in the hands of amateurs who record their work in very fine drawings, one of which is reproduced in Plate V (p. 112). This shows the 30-mile crater Campanus as seen by Mr. L. F. Ball, a well-known member of the Lunar Section of the B.A.A., with a 10 inch telescope and a magnification of 350. Night after night these enthusiasts patiently scrutinise the lesser known parts of the surface, and each year brings forth a crop of new features to add to the many hundreds already known on the face of our satellite.

The Earth-Moon System

In the last section of this chapter we shall consider the earth and the moon together, for they have a number of effects on one another. In general the moon is not in the plane of the ecliptic, but it does cross that plane twice a month, so it is possible for these two bodies and the sun to lie in a straight line when the moon is new or full. This gives rise to eclipses, when at new moon our satellite is seen to move across the face of the sun, an event of great significance to primitive peoples. As the angular diameter of both disks is about half a degree the sun may be completely covered and the eclipse is said to be total. The earth and moon are solid bodies and cast shadows, Fig. 31,

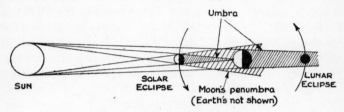

Fig. 31. Solar and lunar eclipses

and the source of light, the sun, being larger than either the shadows are cones. Owing to the varying distance of the sun these cones are not always of the same length, but they are about 233,000 and 850,000 miles respectively. Consider the lunar shadow first, the cause of a solar eclipse, and let us suppose that the eclipse is always central, i.e. that the three bodies form an exact straight line. Now the moon's distance varies from 222,000 to 253,000 miles, so the complete shadow cone, the umbra, may or may not reach the earth's surface in a circular dark patch of the order of 30 miles in diameter. If it does the inhabitants of the patch will see the sun completely covered, a scene of great beauty and, as will be shown later, of importance in solar research. While the eclipse is in progress the shadow will, of course, move, so that the circle becomes drawn out into an eclipse track several thousand miles long. It is a narrow track and does not cross the same spot very often, so astronomers who wish to see it have to pack up their equipment and travel to outlandish places. The 1927 eclipse track crossed Britain from Wales to the Dur-

ham coast; the next British one will be in Cornwall in
1999. Observers outside this totality belt will be in the
half shadow, or penumbra, and will see the sun partly
covered; this is a partial eclipse. Now if the distance of
the moon is greater than the 233,000 miles the point of
the cone will not reach the earth; observers will see the
moon exactly in front of the sun but too small to cover it
and leaving a bright rim all around, the annular eclipse.
When the eclipse is total, darkness falls, the stars come out,
there is a drop in temperature, the birds are hushed, and
the delicate outer appendages of the sun become visible.
Nothing like this happens at a partial or annular one;
there is just an interesting spectacle for observation through
a piece of smoked glass. We have so far assumed that the
eclipse was central, that the three bodies concerned were
in an exact straight line. If this is not so the shadow cone,
though long enough, might miss the earth altogether and
only a partial eclipse can be seen anywhere.

With the earth's shadow the situation is different. At
a solar eclipse the shadow is small; only over a limited
area of the world can totality be seen, and then only for
a few moments. Now we are concerned with a large
shadow which at the distance of the moon is over 5,000
miles across. Thus the moon can become totally immersed
in it for quite a long time, over an hour, and the phenomenon can be seen from the whole night half of our globe.
If the eclipse is not central the moon may be only partly
covered at the greatest phase, or even just pass through
the penumbra, an event of little interest. When a total
eclipse begins a curved shadow nips a little out of the
full moon and then creeps slowly over it until the whole
disk is covered. The moon does not go out. The atmosphere of the earth refracts the sunlight, or bends it into

the geometrical shadow, and owing to absorption of the bluer wavelengths—as at sunset—the refracted light is reddish. Thus the face of the moon can still be seen as a dim coppery globe, though sometimes bright enough for prominent surface features to be discerned. After a while the shadow begins to move off again and about three hours after the eclipse began the whole silvery disk is clear once more.

It has already been mentioned that the plane of the moon's orbit is inclined to the ecliptic at 5° and that the path of our satellite crosses it at two points called the nodes. If the line of the nodes maintained a constant direction in space there would be two occasions in the year when it pointed directly at the sun, and as eclipses can occur only when the moon is near a node there would be two eclipse 'seasons'. These do not occur on the same dates each year because the nodes are slowly moving about 2° a month, causing the dates to become earlier. This movement of the nodes also makes it possible for a third series of eclipses to begin within 12 months. Quite often when an eclipse occurs at one node the moon is in time to cause one at the other a fortnight later. Thus in 1950 there was an annular eclipse of the sun at the ascending node on March 18 and a total eclipse of the moon at the descending node on April 2. Another pair, with the nodes reversed, occurred on September 12 and 26. There can be three in a series, and as a third season can get into the year there may be a maximum of seven. In 1935 there were the following eclipses:

Jan. 5, Sun; partial	July 16, Moon; total
Jan. 19, Moon; total	July 30, Sun; partial
Feb. 3, Sun; partial	Dec. 25, Sun; annular
June 30, Sun; partial	

Note that the middle one of each group of three was a total lunar eclipse. The minimum number in a year is two, one in each 'season' and both solar; the only eclipses in 1951 were annular eclipses of the sun on March 7 and September 1—dates to compare with 1950 above.

The last point about eclipses is a very interesting cycle called the Saros, known in ancient times and used by the old astronomers for eclipse predictions. We have seen that the moon's nodes make a complete rotation in $18\frac{2}{3}$ years, but the repetition of identical conditions is affected also by the period of revolution of the moon about the earth. Thus similar eclipses occur at intervals of 18 years $11\frac{1}{3}$ days (assuming four leap years), not, as might be expected, in the slightly longer period. Take say, a total eclipse of the sun in the northern hemisphere. After a period of 18 years and 11 days there will be an almost identical event, but owing to the extra $\frac{1}{3}$ day the earth will have turned through $\frac{1}{3}$ of a rotation before the event begins. The totality track will therefore be 120° in longitude west of the former one. Fig. 32 shows a group of four eclipses starting with the British one of 1927 and the similarity is striking. The next after these four will be the Cornwall eclipse of 1999 and readers young enough to be able to see it can work out the date for themselves. Each eclipse of this series is slightly further south than the preceding (some series work northwards), so that in time they will reach the south pole and so come to an end. The series, including a few partial ones at the beginning and end, includes about 60 eclipses and takes over 1,000 years.

The moon is the primary cause of the tides, but the theory is very complicated and it is difficult to give a straightforward descriptive account of even its simpler aspects. The attempt will be made, and readers who are not satisfied and are equipped with just a little mathematics can seek a more exact treatment elsewhere (8), (9).

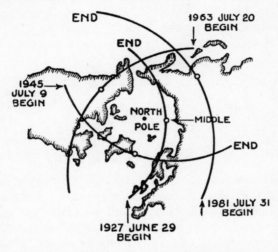

Fig. 32. Some eclipse tracks illustrating the Saros

Suppose that the earth were a sphere uniformly covered with water, Fig. 33, and consider the water at A. The gravitational attraction between two bodies varies inversely as the square of the distance between them. The point A is nearer to the moon than the centre of gravity of the earth C; therefore the force per unit mass on the water at A is greater than on the solid earth behaving as if it were at C. As a result of these forces both the earth and the water will have accelerations towards the moon, the latter being the greater by a quantity *x*. Subtract the earth-acceleration from both; we shall then have an earth with no acceleration and water with an acceleration *x* towards the right. Now this acceleration can be divided into two components, one perpendicular to the earth's surface and of little interest at the moment, and a tangential one AM. Thus the water has a tendency to flow towards the point nearest to the moon. Considering the water at B the acceleration of the earth towards the moon will

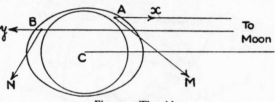

Fig. 33.   The tides

be greater than that of the water by a quantity *y*, because the earth is now nearer than the water. Subtract the earth-acceleration from both and we again get an earth with no acceleration, and water with an acceleration −*y*, i.e. an acceleration of *y* away from the moon. This has a component BN, causing the water to flow to the point furthest from the moon. The final result is that the water is no longer uniformly distributed, but is deepest along the earth-moon axis and shallowest in a perpendicular direction. As the earth rotates these tidal humps would run over the surface of the water and cause two high tides a day at any particular point on the solid earth. We must now remember that the earth is not covered all over with water, the water is not of uniform depth, the tidal motion has to compete with the rotational motion, and there are numerous and large obstructions in the form of land masses. These effects are briefly discussed in the corresponding book on the sea (10). It should already be obvious that tidal prediction is a complicated business, and it depends to a considerable extent on past experience at the place concerned. The sun also has a tide-raising effect, though owing to its greater distance from the earth it is less than that of the moon; the latter largely determines the time-table in the manner already explained. When the moon is full or new the tide-raising forces of the sun and moon are in the same direction, giving a rise and fall greater than the average, the spring tides. At the quarters the solar tide partially nullifies the effect of the lunar and we have the neap tides, which do not rise so high nor fall so low as the springs. This part of it, the height of the tide, seems quite simple, but is it? The actual height is a combination of the tide raising forces of two bodies whose distances are constantly varying, one in an annual cycle and the other in a monthly one. Neither of these bodies move in the plane of the equator; one varies in position from $23\frac{1}{2}°$N. to $23\frac{1}{2}°$S. in half a year, and the other may be anywhere from $28\frac{1}{2}°$N. to $28\frac{1}{2}°$S. The heights are also greatly affected by the shape of the coastline, and their prediction is just as difficult as the time-table. Here we have the moon and tides at London Bridge taken at random from the 1951 Whitaker's Almanack, and although the simple theory would not give the real times of the tides there is some correlation between high water and the moon. Readers at the seaside should make a similar and longer table for their own coast and see if they can find any general local rules.

	Date	Phase	South at	Morning	High Tide feet	Afternoon	feet
Jan.	7	New	11-57 a.m.	12-43	20.9	1-13	21.6
„	15	1st Q.	6-21 p.m.	6-44	19.5	7-32	18.7
„	23	Full	12-6 a.m.	1-57	20.4	2-20	20.9
„	30	3rd Q.	5-28 a.m.	5-50	20.6	6-30	19.7

Throughout most of this chapter the motion of the moon has been regarded as around the earth, and in Fig. 29 the earth was assumed to have a steady orbit and the moon a wavy one. These assumptions are unjustified for the earth is not fixed. When a pair of bodies are revolving in space the forces are mutual and they both move around their common centre of gravity. The common centre of

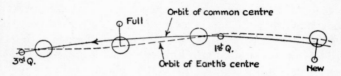

Fig. 34. The motion of the earth-moon system

gravity of two spheres divides the line joining their centres in the inverse ratio of their masses, and since the earth is the more massive of the two bodies under discussion, the point we are looking for must be near the earth end of the line. It is, in fact, within the earth about 3,000 miles from the centre. Thus it is not only the moon that weaves its way in and out of the elliptic orbit around the sun, for on a much smaller scale the earth is doing it too, Fig. 34. At 1st quarter the earth is ahead of its estimated position, now occupied by the common centre, and at 3rd quarter behind. This alternate hurrying and lagging behind due to the moon causes irregularities in the apparent motion of the sun in the ecliptic. These irregularities can be measured; from this the distance of the earth's centre from the common centre can be deduced; from this the ratio of masses of earth and moon can be found; its value is 81:1, and since the mass of the earth is already known, that of the moon can be found.

V

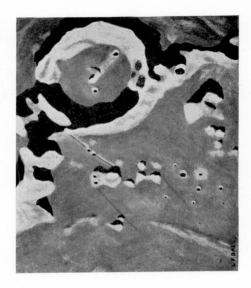

An amateur's drawing: Campanus
Drawing by L. F. Ball

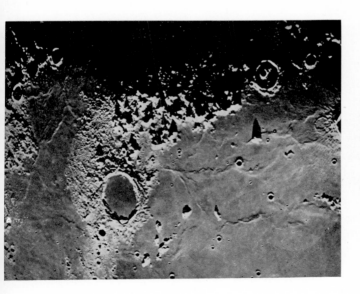

Sunset on the Alps
Lick Observatory Photograph

VI

THE PLANETS

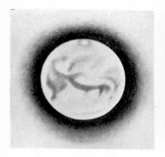

A. Mars: 1941, Sept. 30

B. Saturn: 1948, April 18

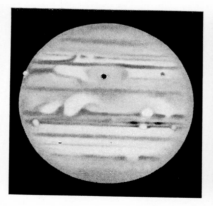

C. Jupiter: 1942, Jan. 6

D. Jupiter: 1927, Oct. 2

Drawings by: A, F. J. Hargreaves; B, R. H. Whittome; C, F. J. Hargreaves.
(*Reproduced from Memoirs of B.A.A.*). D, Lick Observatory Photograph

The problem of the structure and age of the earth properly belongs to geology, but some brief mention must be made here as it is intended in the last chapter to look at the unsolved mystery of its origin. Knowing the size and dimensions of the earth, the average specific gravity can be found. This comes to about 5·5, meaning that on an average the material of the earth is 5·5 times as heavy as water. The ordinary materials of the crust, limestone, granite and so on, have specific gravities lying in the 2-3 region, so that it is clear that there must be something very massive lower down. Evidence available at the present time shows that the crust is quite thin, certainly not exceeding 50 miles; oxygen is the most plentiful element in its rocks, with silicon second and aluminium a bad third. Below that comes the material that occasionally makes its way to the surface as a volcanic outburst. Temperature rises with increasing depth, but this basaltic layer is under very great pressure and it is likely that it liquifies only when the pressure is eased by a rupture in the crust above. It is further supposed that there is a central core about 4,000 miles in diameter composed of metallic material of which iron and nickel, with specific gravities of 7·9 and 8·9 respectively are favoured, though it may be of crustal material changed in some way by great pressure. Between this core and the basaltic layer there is some transitional mixture of unknown composition.

It appears probable that the moon has a common origin with the earth, though to say that it has 'broken off the earth' is going rather far. The suggestion that it came out of the Pacific Ocean is also untenable, as the irregularities on the earth's surface are negligible compared with the size of either body, and if, as is generally supposed, the two bodies are the result of the fission of a larger one when in a fluid state, the said irregularities did not exist at the relevant time. The specific gravity of the moon is about 3·4, suggesting that it is largely composed of rocky material without the metallic core. This, in turn, suggests that the smaller product of the fission was formed mainly from the outer parts of the original body, leaving the denser material at the centre to form the core of the earth.

The age of the earth has been estimated in various ways, and agreement is good enough for this to be no longer classed as an unsolved mystery. A straightforward geological method is as follows: Many rocks of the present time are sedimentary; they were laid down as deposits in water. The thickness of the deposits is known; the rate of deposition going on now is also known; assuming that the rate has always been the same, the time when it began can be estimated at a minimum of several hundred million years. A physical method has been made possible by the discovery of radioactivity. Certain heavy elements, of which radium is the best known, are spontaneously disintegrating at a definite and measurable rate, giving rise to certain radiations and leaving another element as a residue. One of these radioactive elements is uranium, of which the end product is lead, fortunately a slightly different form from ordinary lead and therefore identifiable as ex-uranium. The rate of disintegration of uranium is known, so if an ore containing this element and its end product be analysed their proportions will indicate the age of the rock. From this and similar evidence it appears that the solidification of the earth's crust occurred at least 2,000 million years ago and possibly as many as 3,500 million.

There are several conservation laws in physics, and one of these is the conservation of angular momentum, meaning, rather crudely, that what you gain on the swings you must lose on the roundabouts, and vice versa. The angular momentum of the earth-moon system, which is a constant, is made up of two parts, revolution and rotation, and a reduction in one necessarily means a gain in the other. Consider the tides; this constant pulling of the waters to the earth-moon axis against their natural tendency to rotate with the earth is acting as a brake. Thus the day is very slowly getting longer (about $\frac{1}{1000}$ sec. per century). This means the spin momentum is decreasing; therefore the revolution momentum must increase by the expedient of the moon moving further away and taking a slightly longer month. Calculating backwards in time it has been estimated that 4,000 million years ago the two bodies were nearly in contact and the revolution and rotation periods were both four hours. This must have been when our hypothetical fluid parent divided and it is not surprising that it did. If a body larger than the earth was rotating at that rate the centrifugal (outward) force must have been terrific. Working onwards in time it appears that in 50,000 million years the distance of the moon will be about 350,000 miles and the day and the month will both be 47 of our present days. A tidal effect due to the sun will then operate to bring the moon nearer until at about 10,000 miles it will fall to pieces* and the earth-moon system will come to an end.

* See the formation of Saturn's rings in the next chapter.

REFERENCES

(1) G. W. Tyrrell, *The Earth and its Mysteries*, 1953.

(2) See Sir William Bragg, *The Universe of Light*, 1933, or

(3) M. Minneart, *Light and Colour in the Open Air*, 1940.

(4) C. M. Botley, *The Air and its Mysteries*.

(5) See correspondence in *The Observatory*, Nos 855-857, 1950.

(6) Reliable popular reading on this topic: A. C. Clarke, *The Exploration of Space*, 1951.

(7) Bonestell's drawings are nearer the truth; see Bonestell and Ley, *The Conquest of Space*, 1950.

(8) M. Davidson, *From Atoms to Stars*, 1946.

(9) Barlow and Bryan, *Mathematical Astronomy*, 1944.

(10) J. S. Colman, *The Sea and its Mysteries*, 1950.

(11) For a general description of the Moon see H. P. Wilkins, *Our Moon*, or P. Moore, *Guide to the Moon*, both 1954.

CHAPTER V

The Sun's Family

IN previous chapters we have been introduced to the family, and are already fairly familiar with their names and behaviour. It now remains to meet them as individuals, taking first the larger members, the planets.

While discussing the motions, real and apparent, of the planets the natural division was between those whose orbits lie within that of the earth, and those outside. Now it is more convenient to make another division, the nature of which should be clear from the accompanying table.

Name	Mean distance from sun in millions of miles	Period		Diameter in miles	Density relative to water	Number of satellites
		Revolution	Rotation			
Mercury	36	88 days	88 days	3,000	3·73	0
Venus	67	225 ,,	225 ,, (?)	7,600	5·21	0
Earth	93	1 year	23 h. 56 m.	7,927*	5·52	1
Mars	142	1 yr. 322 d.	24 h. 37 m.	4,200	3·94	2
Jupiter	483	12 years	about 10 h.	88,700*	1·34	12
Saturn	866	29 ,,	10 h. 14 m.	75,100*	0·69	9
Uranus	1783	84 ,,	about 10¾ h.	30,900	1·36	5
Neptune	2794	165 ,,	15 h. 40 m.	33,000	1·32	2
Pluto	3666	248 ,,	unknown	about 3,650	—	0

* Equatorial

There is a considerable gap in distance between Mars and Jupiter, and a corresponding jump in period of revolution. Compared with the first four, the second four are much larger but considerably less dense, they have a high speed of rotation on their axes; and they are plentifully endowed with satellites. With Pluto there appears to be a return to group 1. The earth is a typical member of group 1, and with the general character of that body still fresh in mind let us examine the individual characteristics of the other three—Pluto being excluded for the present.

Mercury, Venus, and Mars

Mercury and Venus, having orbits within that of the earth, both undergo the alternations of morning and evening star and exhibit phases (see p. 36) but with the marked difference that Mercury is as elusive as Venus is prominent. Venus is at the greater distance from the sun and at the time of greatest elongation is situated in our sky about 47° from it. The orbit of Venus is nearly a circle, and thus successive elongations do not differ very much among themselves. The maximum elongation for Mercury is only 28°, so that it is never very far from the horizon at sunrise or sunset and in high latitudes like ours is not seen in a dark sky. Added to this are the facts that it is a smaller planet and is further from the earth; its magnitude (1) at elongation lies between +0·57 and − 0·24 compared with about − 4·0 for Venus. The orbit of Mercury is very eccentric, so that its distance from the sun varies over a range of 15 million miles and the elongation angle can be under 18°—and the planet is difficult enough to see at 28°. Thus this planet is rarely noticed, but that does not mean that it is not studied, for the properly equipped astronomer can find it in daylight.

The orbit of Mercury is of interest in another respect. The simple planetary theory based on Kepler's laws alone assumes that they move under the influence of the sun alone, but of course the other planets interfere. As a result the axes of the planet's ellipses are slowly changing, and these changes could be successfully predicted by the mathematicians—except for Mercury. Here there was an unexplained discrepancy of 40 seconds of arc per century. When Neptune had been successfully located mathematically, attention was devoted to finding an inner planet that was disturbing Mercury. So great was the confidence that it was given the name Vulcan in anticipation of its discovery. It was not discovered, and when Einstein developed his theory of relativity early in this century he succeeded in making a prediction that was very nearly correct, so that Mercury was able to provide an experimental confirmation of the then new mathematical outlook.

The period of rotation of Mercury upon its axis presents a difficult problem, for the disk is small and such markings as can be made out are too indefinite to be of much value. The period is generally regarded as being 88 days, so that the planet presents one face permanently to the sun, but the fact is not really satisfactorily established. The temperature of the sunlit face will be high. It is possible to measure the radiation from a planet by allowing its telescopic image to fall on a bolometer, an electrical instrument for detecting radiation. Directly reflected solar radiation must be eliminated and a correction applied for the effect of the earth's atmosphere, so it is an experiment of some difficulty. It appears that the temperature in question is about 300-400°C, the varying distance from the sun causing quite a wide range. The absence of atmosphere would be expected;* the moon has lost its surrounding

* Evidence of a trace of atmosphere was found in 1950.

gases because their molecular velocities were quite a high fraction of the velocity of escape, and they will be considerably higher on the hotter Mercury, even though the velocity of escape is higher too. From time to time Mercury and Venus can be seen in transit across the sun's disk. When this occurs a ring of atmosphere can be seen around Venus, but not Mercury. Further, the albedo, or reflecting power of Mercury is low, while for the cloud covered Venus it is high. Of the surface of Mercury we know practically nothing, but we can presume that it is something like that of the moon with an even greater torrid desolation.

The situation with regard to Venus is not much better, even though there is a larger disk for study. The atmosphere is impenetrable to visible light; an infra-red photograph gives a slightly smaller image than the ultra-violet, showing some penetration, but even then not to the solid surface. Such markings as can be seen, and there are some, particularly in the crescent phase, are atmospheric and of doubtful permanence. If the axial rotation was as rapid as our own, as was once believed, the markings should show it. It is generally assumed that Venus, like Mercury, turns the same face to the sun, but if this were so the sunlit and dark hemispheres would be at vastly different temperatures. Experiment, not so difficult this time, shows that the temperature range is quite small. As a planet rotates one limb must be moving away from the observer and one approaching, so that a Doppler shift in the spectrum is to be expected. This too has been tried but results are inconsistent. Opinion today favours a rotation period of about a month. The spectrum of the atmosphere of Venus is interesting in another way; it shows an abundance of carbon dioxide and a deficiency of oxygen and water vapour, but we must remember that this is only the outer layer and the composition, like that of our own atmosphere, may be different at ground level. What is Venus really like? We don't know, but readers who are interested in planetary surfaces should see Bonestell's imaginative but very sensible pictures (2).

Mars, in an orbit outside that of the earth, is at its nearest when fully illuminated, and its phases are limited to a not very obvious gibbous state. Thus it is easier to study than either Mercury or Venus. Since the orbits of Mars and the earth are not concentric circles, but are ellipses, the opposition distance between them varies from 35 to 63 million miles. A favourable 'opposition' (see p. 37) is one occurring when the two planets happen to be at their least distance from one another, as in 1939; the next such occasion will be in 1956 (Fig. 35).

A further advantage is that we can see its surface (Plate VI, p. 113). We know that the rotation period and inclination of the axis to the ecliptic are comparable with those of the earth, and it has seasons, though its year is nearly twice as long as ours. The surface has been carefully studied and for many years maps of the numerous named features have been available (3). The predominant colour is brown and is possibly that of desert areas. The markings of greenish-grey vary slightly in tint with the changes in season, and may therefore be areas in which there is some kind of vegetation. At the poles there are white caps, the southern one being the larger, that also change with the season as would be expected of polar snow caps. The deposition and evaporation of these caps indicate the presence of an atmosphere, and faint patches of cloud are also seen over this planet. The ultra-violet and infra-red photographs provide convincing evidence, for the former gives a larger image and does not show the surface features. These photographs also indicate that the polar caps are, at least in part, an atmospheric phenomenon. The Martian atmosphere is 'of very low density compared with

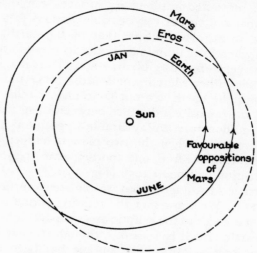

Fig. 35. The orbits of Earth, Mars and Eros

our own and contains very little oxygen. It is a cold planet, the equatorial noon being about equivalent to an autumn day in England.

At the favourable opposition of 1877 Schiaparelli discovered some straight markings that he called 'canali', meaning channels. It was some years before they were seen by anyone else and their real existence has often been doubted. Some of them are now mapped, and traces of them have been detected on the negatives of photographs, so there can be little doubt that the more prominent ones are real features. Even with a large instrument and good conditions Mars looks very small and these features are only at the very threshold of visibility; thus vague mottlings may be mistaken for lines. An illustrative diagram appeared in Hutchinson's *Splendour of the Heavens* (4); one half was made up of apparently random blotches and the other of lines, but they look remarkably alike when viewed from a distance of 30 feet. Unfortunately in the English language a canal is an artificial waterway with locks and barges and so on, and thus the canals of Mars, the supposed artificiality of which had an influential supporter in Lowell, have caught the public interest far more than is justified by their nature.

Mars has two satellites revolving around him in the usual west to east direction, neither being more than about 10 miles in diameter. Phobos is only 5,800 miles from the centre of Mars, and has a period of 7 h. 39 m., so that it would rise in the west and set in the east. Deimos at 14,600 miles has a period of 30 h. 21 m., just over a Martian day; this one would remain above the horizon for nearly three days and over two cycles of phases. The presence of these satellites enables the mass and density of Mars to be found with more confidence than in the cases of the moonless Venus and Mercury.

The internal constitution of the earth was discussed in the last chapter. Venus being similar in size and density may be assumed to be similar in constitution also. The densities of the smaller Mars and Mercury are nearer to that of the moon, and maybe in these bodies the nickel-iron core is absent.

The Four Great Planets

In the second group of planets we have something quite different, not only by virtue of their large size. Their

satellite systems enable masses and densities to be calculated with some accuracy and the mean densities are
found to be low, Saturn being even less massive than an
equal volume of water. The high albedo suggests an
atmospheric surface and the telescopic appearance confirms it. The degree of flattening at the poles is remarkable;
the equatorial and polar diameters of the earth are 7,926
and 7,900 miles respectively—a difference of 0·33%,
whereas the corresponding values for Jupiter are 88,700
and 82,800—a difference of 6·7%. The speed of rotation
is high, but there must also be a considerable degree of
fluidity. To account for the flattening and low density a
probable constitution of Jupiter has been worked out:
a rocky core of about half the planet's diameter, a layer
of ice some 16,000 miles thick, and finally 6,000 miles of
low density atmosphere. The other planets would be
similar but with different proportions; Saturn, with a
slightly slower spin but considerably greater flattening,
must have a greater proportion of atmosphere and a
smaller central core. Now let us consider some of their
individual characteristics.

The feature that at once catches the eye in a telescopic
view of Jupiter is the light and dark cloud belts, going
straight across the disk. The straightness is due, of course,
to the fact that the axis of rotation is very nearly perpendicular to the line of sight from the earth: Observation
of these belts reveals the rotation rate, and the interesting
fact that it varies with latitude, the period being five
minutes longer near the poles than at the equator. Among
these belts are various spots, light or dark, lasting for a
matter of weeks, or perhaps months; the surface is constantly changing, and constantly watched by amateur
observers. The Great Red Spot, which was noticed in

1878, was an oval marking 30,000 miles long, prominent for 30 years, and traces of it still remain. It can be discerned in both pictures, Plate VI (p. 113); in the drawing there is falling upon it the shadow of satellite II, the satellite itself being just in front of the west (left) limb. Radiation measurements show that the temperature of Jupiter is of the order of − 150°C, in agreement with a state of equilibrium in which the planet is radiating just as much energy as it receives—there was a theory at one time that it is hot and radiates more than it receives. The spectroscope indicates the presence of ammonia and methane (marsh gas) in the outer layers of the Jovian atmosphere.

Galileo's discovery of the four great satellites of Jupiter has already been mentioned. In size they are comparable with, though rather larger than, our moon; their distances from the planet range approximately from a quarter of a million to a million miles, and their period of revolution from 42 hours to nearly 17 days. These four are a constant source of joy to the owners of small telescopes; their configurations are constantly changing, they transit in front of the planet or vanish behind him, they may be eclipsed in his shadow, they even eclipse one another. It was the study of these eclipses that gave Romer the clue to the finite velocity of light. There are eight minor satellites, one lying within the orbits of the great four, and one, Jupiter XII, being a very recent discovery by Nicholson of Mount Wilson, who found it photographically on September 9, 1951 (5).

Of the surface of Saturn one can say 'like Jupiter only less so'. In this case there was a Great White Spot in 1933, but it was not really the spot which was of significance—there had been such spots before—but the fact that it was discovered by a famous actor of stage and screen, for the late Will Hay was also an able amateur astronomer. The great feature of Saturn is its wonderful and unique ring system, three of them lying in the plane of the equator. There is an outer bright ring, then a small gap, followed by a wider bright ring and an innermost dusky one (Plate VI, p. 113). The plane of the rings is inclined to the ecliptic, so that in the course of one revolution of 29 years we see first one side and then the other. They are extremely thin and when edge on they are invisible for a short period. There is also an aspect when they are illuminated from one side and we see them from the other. They were edge on in 1950 and we now see the north side at a steadily increasing angle.

A point of importance is their structure. If the rings were solid and were revolving around the planet the rim would move faster than the inner edge. The spectroscope and Doppler's principle show that the contrary is the case; the outer part moves more slowly as in the case of a system of satellites. Thus the rings are composed of myriads of small fragments circulating around the planet. It can be proved mathematically that a satellite would be unstable if it were too close to its primary, and there is a definite critical distance for each planet known as Roche's limit. All known satellites lie outside the appropriate limit, but Saturn's rings lie within it and therefore would appear to be the debris of a satellite that trespassed within the forbidden region. A difficulty is that it is unlikely that the debris would be as small as those believed to compose the ring. Saturn has nine ordinary satellites of which the brightest is Titan, a little larger than the moon and the sixth out from Saturn. These satellites are of special interest to mathematicians.

Uranus and Neptune are too far away for much to be seen of surface detail, so we will confine our attention to their satellites. Four satellites of Uranus have been known for over a century. Their orbits lie approximately in the plane of the planet's equator, but as the axis of rotation is nearly parallel to the plane of the ecliptic these satellites move very nearly perpendicular to it. The satellite of Neptune was discovered almost as soon as the planet. Its plane is inclined to the ecliptic at 35° and its motion is retrograde, i.e. opposite from most of the others. Certain of the lesser satellites of Jupiter and Saturn have retrograde orbits and, for reasons that we need not go into here, the same applies to all four of Uranus. Both planets, however, have had recent additions to their families, but they do not yet appear in many published lists. On photographs taken at the McDonald Observatory, U.S.A., a new satellite of Uranus was found in 1948, and for Neptune in 1949. The other satellites of Uranus are given Shakespearian names, Titania, Oberon, etc., so the new one is called Miranda, and Nereid has been suggested for the companion of Triton, Neptune's other satellite.

The Minor Planets

Apologies will be due to the God of the Underworld for mentioning Pluto in this section. The Minor Planets or Asteroids are small objects with eccentric orbits lying mainly in the gap between those of Mars and Jupiter. Pluto is not one of them, but in some respects this outermost planet behaves like them. The eccentricity of its orbit is 0·25; the largest of the others are Mercury, 0·21 and Mars, 0·09. The plane of its orbit is inclined to the ecliptic at an angle of 17°, whereas that for Mercury is 7° and all the others are less than half that of Mercury. The stellar magnitude of Pluto is about 14, while its neighbour Neptune is within reach of a pair of binoculars at magnitude 8. Needless to say very little is known of this planet. From its magnitude and an assumed albedo it was deduced to be rather smaller than the earth, for it was too small to measure directly. In March 1950, with the 200 inch telescope, a successful measurement was made; this is quoted in the table at the beginning of the chapter. When the existence of the unknown planet was predicted a mass of about six times that of the earth was expected. Once the planet had been found it was realised that the mass could hardly exceed about 0·7 of the earth and its apparent effect on Neptune calls for 0·8. Now that the diameter is really known it appears that to achieve such a mass the density of Pluto would have to be about 40 relative to water, and uranium, the heaviest of all elements, is only 18·7! The mass of Pluto is probably about one tenth of the earth, too small to cause much inconvenience to Uranus or Neptune. There is no evidence of an atmosphere and, as yet, no satellite. The temperature in the region of Pluto can be expected to be about − 220°C.

The discovery of the genuine asteroids is mentioned in Ch. II. There were originally four, all circulating in the expected place between Mars and Jupiter, and these are the four largest:

Ceres:	480 miles diam;	opposition magnitude	(1951)	7.9
Pallas:	306 ,, ,,	,,	,,	,, 9.2
Juno:	121 ,, ,,	,,	,,	,, 10.0
Vesta:	241 ,, ,,	,,	,,	(1950) 7.0

Under favourable conditions Vesta can be just bright enough to see with the naked eye, and Pallas held for many years the record for inclination to the ecliptic, 35°

October 3rd.   Large Scale

October 30th.   Small Scale
Comet Morehouse 1908.   *Photographed at the Royal Observatory, Greenwich*

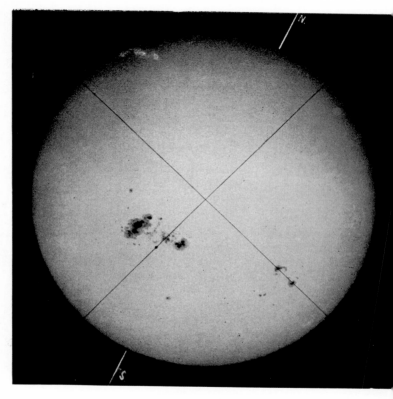

The sun, 1947, April 6
Cape Observatory

—minor planets are not confined to the Zodiac. No one could realise at the time that the ultimate number would run into thousands, and thus the system of naming after female deities was adopted. The supply of such names has long since given out and it is doubtful whether it is wise to try to find names at all, for there were 275 new planets in 1949 alone! Most of the asteroids are small, less than 50 miles in diameter and some, perhaps, as small as a mile. There is also evidence to suggest that some of them are irregular in shape. Some of their orbits are of high eccentricity and are very much the same as comet orbits. The original four and many others, keep their place between Mars and Jupiter, but there are many that do not. Hermes, for example, has its perihelion within the orbit of Venus, and at its crossing of the earth's path in 1937 it came to within 400,000 miles of the earth itself and could actually be watched moving across its starry background. Hidalgo, an opposite example, moves out very nearly to the orbit of Saturn and beats Pallas comfortably with an inclination of 43°. The chief interest in the minor planets is statistical, which would be out of place in this book; a very readable paper on minor planets in general has been given recently as a presidential address before the British Astronomical Association (6).

One more asteroid must be discussed because it is associated with our long deferred problem of the measurement of the distance of the sun. Eros was discovered in 1898 and is a faint object about 17 miles in diameter, but its importance lies in the fact that its orbit carries it at perihelion within the orbit of Mars, giving a possible close approach to the earth. A favourable approach, to a distance of 14,000,000 miles, occurred in 1931 and gave an opportunity for re-determining the distance of the sun.

I

The determination of the distance of the moon was given in Ch. IV; it was based on measuring the apparent positions of the moon as seen from two stations a known distance apart. The solution of the problem was then a trigonometric one similar to that of a terrestrial surveyor. This method cannot be applied to the sun; the distance is too great. The mean radius of the earth's orbit is called the 'astronomical unit'. Let us forget about miles and call the earth's distance 1·0 as we did on page 42. The relative distances of the planets from the sun can be found by a combination of observation and geometry; such work also gives the eccentricities of the planetary orbits and the direction of the major axes, so that a complete plan can be made on a scale of so many inches to the astronomical unit. Fig. 35 was drawn from such information. It is thus possible for any distance in the solar system to be read off the drawing or calculated in astronomical units; an example would be the opposition distance of Mars. Now if this can also be measured in miles by the trigonometric method we have our scale, the astronomical unit will be expressed in miles and our problem solved. This has been done, but even at a favourable opposition the distance to be measured is 35 million miles. The position of Venus on the sun's disk when in transit has also been used, but the distance again is large. Eros in 1931 provided a distance of 14 million, and numerous observatories co-operated in taking photographs for position. The Astronomer Royal, Sir Harold Spencer Jones, correlated their results and the astronomical unit was found to be 93,005,000 miles. The angle subtended at the sun by the earth's semi-diameter is called the Solar Parallax, and the new value for this quantity is 8″·790.

Comets

Not all bodies moving in eccentric orbits are minor planets—completely solid bodies giving point images on photographic plates. Some are comets, diffuse in appearance and probably in structure also. They are temporary visitors to our sky because it is only when near perihelion that they are bright enough to be seen. The main part of a comet is the head, a disk of hazy light, and this can usually be recognised, at least when the comet is at its best, as a bright central nucleus surrounded by a less bright area called the coma. In addition there may be a tail, either a hazy structureless one or a clear collection of rays and streamers as seen in Plate VII (p. 128). The mass of a comet is believed to be small, for when a comet passes near a planet, even a small one, it is pulled a little out of its orbit by the force of gravitation but, although forces act both ways, no effect on the planet can be detected. On the other hand their linear dimensions are quite large; they vary very widely, but as a rough idea the nucleus can be regarded as hundreds of miles in diameter, the whole head a matter of a few thousand, and the length of the tail a few million. The mean density, then, must be very small; according to some authorities that of the head is about the same as a fairly respectable vacuum! The nucleus is presumed to consist of a cloud of stones and the coma, which gives a bright line spectrum, to be mainly gaseous and containing metallic vapours. The tail was formerly believed to be gaseous also, but it seems probable that it is composed, at least in part, of extremely fine particles having dimensions of the order of a thousandth of a millimetre. The brightness of a comet is due partly to reflected sunlight and partly to some self-luminosity of unknown origin, both parts being increased by proximity to the sun.

When a comet has been observed for a few weeks it becomes possible for the mathematicians to calculate the orbit, expecting to find an eccentricity between 0·5 and 1·0 (c.f. 0·09 for Mars and 0·25 for Pluto). The higher the number the longer the ellipse, and hence the longer the period that must elapse before the comet returns to perihelion. These periods, like those of the planets, differ greatly from one another. If the eccentricity is exactly equal to 1·0 the curve is not an ellipse, but a parabola, and if greater than 1·0 it indicates a hyperbola. The precise nature of these curves need not detain us. It is sufficient to say that they are not closed curves at all; the comet will therefore never come back—which raises the interesting and unanswerable question, 'Where did it come from anyway?' Orbits are sometimes changed by a close approach to the planet; Jupiter, for instance, appears to have collected about 30 comets which now have orbits lying just about within his own.

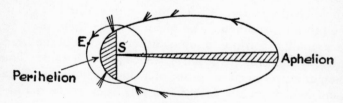

Fig. 36. The orbit of a comet

Let us consider a period in the life of a great comet, beginning at aphelion (Fig. 36). In accordance with Kepler's second law, the radius vector sweeps over equal areas in equal times, so the motion is very slow; a comet lingers a long time in the remote part of its orbit. As time passes it accelerates and gets nearer the sun. The temperature rises, occluded gases begin to leave the stony nucleus and form the coma, and eventually it becomes bright enough for a hazy spot of, perhaps, the 15th magnitude, to be picked up in the telescope. Nearer the sun: the head gets larger and brighter, and now a new force comes into play. Light, or rather radiation, can exert a pressure. This pressure is very small, but it has been shown that for very minute particles it can exceed gravitational attraction. Thus such particles begin to leave the head and stream out in a direction away from the sun. As perihelion is approached the head gets brighter and brighter, it surpasses the first magnitude and may even be visible in daylight, while the tail, sweeping around always away from the sun, is like a searchlight beam in the night sky and many millions of miles long. When perihelion is passed the splendour begins to fade. The tail diminishes, the head fades, and the comet once more vanishes into obscurity. A great comet is not a common occurrence and it is many years since observers in the northern hemisphere witnessed such a spectacle. Nevertheless comets in general are quite frequent; for instance in 1949, an average year, 20 were under observation and five of these were new.

Now we leave the hypothetical comet and look at some real ones. The question is 'which'? Apart from Halley's comet there would be as many choices as there are authors and I shall speak of only three. Edmund Halley, Astronomer Royal from 1720 to 1742, noticed that the orbits of the comets of 1531, 1607 and 1682 were similar, and it occurred to him that they were successive returns of the same comet. He predicted that it would return again in

1758 or 1759, knowing, of course, that he could not live to see this fulfilled. On Christmas Day 1758 the discovery was made, and the object passed perihelion in the following March. The first periodic comet had been discovered. It has been traced back to 240 B.C. and there is some historic record of every apparition but one. This is the comet that worried King Harold before the Norman Conquest (Fig. 4); it is also the comet that appeared in A.D. 66 and was regarded by early historians as having foretold the approaching destruction of Jerusalem (7). In its last appearance, 1910, it was not seen to the best advantage in northern latitudes but was nevertheless a fine spectacle. The close approach on May 18 was of interest, particularly to the end-of-the-world people. The earth and comet were moving in opposite directions, for this comet, like some others, moves in a retrograde path, and our globe swept through the great tail containing the poisonous cyanogen—and nothing happened at all! Since the tail points away from the sun the head must have been in transit over the sun's disk, but nothing could be seen and this gives a useful confirmation of the scattered nature of the material of the nucleus.

Morehouse's comet of 1908 was not a bright one, but it was a particularly good subject for photography. A long series of photographs were taken, two of which are reproduced in Plate VII (p. 128), and they provided students of astronomy with material of outstanding value. The tail was remarkable both for its fan-like structure and for the rapidity of its changes; the fan is shown in our first picture. The spread of the fan varied; at one time the tail appeared twisted; at another it looked rather like the flame discharging from a rocket; at one stage the comet seemed to be throwing away one tail and growing another. Our second picture is, of course, taken on a different date, but is also a different kind of photograph. The first is on a large scale and is 1° square, while the second is on a small scale and is 10° square (see p. 67). The apparatus was following the rapidly moving comet, so the star images have trailed, though it is hardly noticeable in the small scale example.

Whipple's comet of 1942-3 was a very ordinary representative of the species, but it was one that the public could see, and in a prominent place. The writer remembers well a boy, who knew the stars vaguely and comets not at all, bursting into his study to say that 'there is something in the middle of the Plough'. It was visible for some weeks, it reached a magnitude of 3·9 and a short tail could be seen with binoculars. While visible it passed right through a very familiar star field and was moving fast enough for changes to be noted from night to night.

On November 1st 1948 a total eclipse of the sun took place, visible only in the southern hemisphere. When the moment of darkness came there, not far from the sun, was an unexpected comet! About a week later it was seen in the morning twilight, of the first magnitude and with a tail 25° long (8). It remained visible to the naked eye for about a month, but had fallen to the 8th magnitude by the time it had moved sufficiently far north to be visible in England. Its official title is Comet 1948*l*, and popularly the 'Eclipse Comet'.

Meteors

The nature of a shooting star was mentioned in the first chapter; it is a small solid fragment, ordinarily ranging in size from a grain of sand to a pea. They enter the earth's atmosphere at a high velocity, which is then checked by air resistance. Since the kinetic energy of the particle is being lost some other form of energy must take its place, and heat is the result, its production being assumed to be due to the compression of the air in front of the particle; all users of a bicycle pump know that compression produces heat. However, the heating effect is so great that the particle is raised to incandescence and is vaporised, sometimes leaving a train of sparks behind. Serious meteor observing requires considerable skill, for in a fraction of time it is necessary to note where among the stars the path began and ended, the time at which it occurred, and the duration of flight. If two observers some miles apart have recorded the same meteor, the height and velocity can be calculated. Results vary, of course, but to give an idea it would be reasonable to say that they are first observed at a height of about 75 miles and have burnt out at 45 miles, travelling a considerable horizontal distance in the interval, with a velocity of some 25 miles per second. Cameras can also be used for recording meteor tracks; a meteor track can be seen in Plate XI (p. 176).

Larger meteors, say of cricket ball size, become visible at a greater altitude and fall much lower. They also break up explosively and the phenomenon, this time known as a fire-ball, is both spectacular and noisy. Meteors are very numerous. An observer settling down to watch for one hour might see anything from six to 60, but he observes only quite a small area. The total number arriving per day must run into millions, but the vast majority of them are rendered harmless by the protective mantle of our atmosphere. From time to time meteorites weighing anything from grains to tons do strike the ground and fragments can afterwards be picked up. Some are entirely stony, some metallic—chiefly iron and nickel, and some a combination of the two. Large meteorites are fortunately very rare. One fell in a sparsely inhabited part of Siberia in 1908 and when, some years later, the occurrence was fully investigated it was found that trees had been felled for many miles around, with their trunks pointing away from the point of impact, and the area scorched by the heat was as big as quite a large town. In February 1947 there was another, near the Pacific coast of the U.S.S.R. (9). Again trees were uprooted, and the explosion was heard for 60 miles and the light seen for over 100. It was an iron meteorite that broke up, there being 30 craters in all, up to 75 feet in diameter and 27 feet deep.

If the apparent paths of meteors seen in one evening be plotted on a star chart and produced backwards, many of them will meet fairly closely at one point. Those that do, belong to a stream or shower and the point is called the radiant. It is the point in space from which this particular shower is coming in parallel paths, the apparent divergence from the radiant being due to perspective. These meteor streams are moving in orbits similar to those of comets and the showers are seen on those dates when the earth is at the intersection of its own orbit and theirs. In some cases the meteors seem to be well spread along their paths, giving similar displays each year; in other cases they are bunched, giving specially good displays at certain intervals of years. The Leonids, so called because the radiant is in the constellation of Leo, appear each year in November, but used to be brilliant in quantity and quality at intervals of 33 years. The brilliant displays now seem to have ceased. Some meteor orbits are almost identical with certain comets, and it is suggested that the meteors are debris left behind by the comet. It is further suggested that in orbits where there is now no comet there was one once, and there is a case in support of that argument. Biela's comet, with a period of $6\frac{3}{4}$ years, was quite normal in 1832; it was not seen in 1839 owing to being badly placed, and in 1846 it had divided into two. On its next return the two were widely separated. It has never been seen again, but three returns later, in 1872, there was a great meteor display, and each year in November Bielid meteors are seen with a radiant in Andromeda. In addition to the regular streams there are sporadic meteors, sometimes with higher velocities and apparently with hyperbolic orbits; these, presumably, are intruders from outer space and do not belong to the sun's family.

Now we come to something quite new: the study of meteors by day as well as by night, using radar instead of the eye or the camera. The principle of radar, that device that so much helped the 'Few' to win the Battle of Britain, is this. A narrow beam of short-wave wireless radiation is projected, almost like a searchlight, and if it strikes an aircraft some of the energy is reflected back. The time interval between the radio pulse, which travels with the speed of light, and the echo is automatically recorded and converted into distance. The direction and elevation of the transmission being known, the position of the aircraft is fixed. Now a meteor leaves an ionised trail behind it —the nature of ionisation will be explained later—and this also will reflect radio waves. Thus the meteor trail can be picked up in daylight or through cloud as well as on a clear night. This ionisation had been discovered as long ago as 1932, but it was the rapid development of radar during the war that made its exploitation so successful. In 1945 Hey and Stewart, working with a wavelength of 4-5 metres and a beam width of 30° found that re-flections were received when visible meteors crossed the

beam, thus confirming that it really was meteor trails that
they were detecting. They also found that best results were
obtained when the trail was perpendicular to the beam.
The following year they succeeded in finding by radio
methods the velocities of the Giacobinid meteors; their
results gave 22·9 metres per second with a possible error
of 1·3 metres. This compares favourably with the accepted
value of 23·7 metres and demonstrates the validity of the
new method. Echoes were more numerous than visible
meteors, possibly owing to the fact that some trails strong
enough to reflect the radio waves were too faint to see.
Two other groups of workers were also studying this
shower, and since then radio astronomy has been taken
up comprehensively by Lovell and others at the Jodrell
Bank research station of the University of Manchester. In
1948 Clegg devised a method of finding the radiant of the
trails, and subsequently the Jodrell Bank party found a
new shower radiating from Pisces, and later another in
Gemini, observable in daylight only (10), (11), (12). It is
interesting to add that in 1946 the U.S. Signal Corps
succeeded in receiving radar echoes from the moon, using
a wavelength of 2·7 metres (13). Echoes have also been
obtained from the Aurora.

Zodiacal Light

This is a faint band of light spreading along the ecliptic
away from the sun, in the evening in the west and in the
early morning in the east. It is best seen when the ecliptic
makes a large angle with the horizon, as in spring evenings
and autumn mornings (Fig. 27), and best of all in the
tropics. The theory is that the sun is surrounded by a large
thin disk of minute particles, and we see light scattered by
these. It is estimated that particles 1 mm. in diameter

spaced at distances of 5 yards would be sufficient to explain the phenomenon.

REFERENCES

(1) A brief but interesting paper on the brightness of Mercury is given by M. B. B. Heath in *Journal of B.A.A.*, 61/43, 1951.

(2) Bonestell and Ley, *The Conquest of Space*, 1950. This book is about inter-planetary travel but includes numerous pictures of what the traveller may expect to see.

(3) A recent map appears in the new edition of Ball's *Popular Guide to the Heavens*, and another in *Memoirs of the B.A.A.*, Vol. 37, Part 1.

(4) Also reproduced in M. Davidson, *From Atoms to Stars*, 1946.

(5) See popular account by the discoverer himself, *Sky and Telescope*, XI/79, 1952.

(6) J. G. Porter, *Journal of the B.A.A.*, 61/4, 1950. There is also an interesting chapter on this topic in Ref. 2.

(7) A short history of this comet is given in J. E. Gore, *Studies in Astronomy*, 1904. Also in Hutchinson's *Splendour of the Heavens*.

(8) Detailed account in the *Journal of the B.A.A.*, 60/240, 1950.

(9) Brief account and comment in *Discovery*, VIII/176, 1947.

(10) A technical account of the whole work is given by J. S. Hey in *Monthly Notices of R.A.S.*, 109/179, 1949.

(11) J. G. Porter on the Daylight Meteors, *Journal of B.A.A.*, 58/50, 1948, is easier reading for the layman.

(12) Popular account by A. C. B. Lovell, *Discovery*, XII/7, 1951.

(13) A recent experiment of this kind is described in *Sky and Telescope*, XI/194, 1952.

(14) For further reading on the planets see P. Moore, *Guide to the Planets*, 1955, or the relevant chapters of *Everyman's Astronomy*, edited by M. Davidson, 1952.

CHAPTER VI

The Sun and Other Stars

THE last two chapters have been devoted to astronomical bodies, including the one on which we live, which have little or no energy of their own. They are dependent upon the sun, and the light by which we see them initially came from the sun. The sun itself is in a different class; it is one of the vast multitude of self-luminous spheres, the stars, which in some mysterious way produce energy and radiate it out into space year after year for almost countless time. How they do it is a problem for the final chapter; here we are concerned with the facts of their appearance and behaviour. One of the stars, the sun, is very much nearer than the rest. Light reaches us from it in about 8 minutes, whereas the corresponding time for the next star is over 4 years. The apparent brightness of the stars varies over a very wide range, from magnitude − 1·6 to magnitude 21 (see p. 75), excluding the sun at − 26. The differences are not all due to varying distance for the intrinsic brightness varies too. Some stars emit more light than the sun, others less; some are larger or hotter than the sun, others less so. The sun is an average member of its class, and we are fortunate in having an average example close at hand for detailed examination.

The Sun

The sun is a sphere which seen from the earth subtends an angle of about half a degree, this angle varying slightly according to the position of the earth in its orbit. The distance corresponding to the exact angle at any instant is calculable, and it is thus possible to determine the actual diameter of this sphere. It is 864,000 miles; this is 108 times the diameter of the earth and not far short of double the diameter of the moon's orbit. It has already been explained how the masses of the earth and moon can be obtained. We know, from the velocity of the earth in its orbit, the acceleration of the earth towards the sun, and we also know the distance from the sun. An application of the formula on p. 88 then gives us the mass of the sun, which is about 333,000 times greater than that of the earth, or nearly 2×10^{27} tons. Obviously tons are of little use for astronomical purposes, and throughout the remainder of this book the unit of mass will be the sun itself—our scale will be sun = 1. The volume of the sun is greater than the earth in the ratio $(108)^3$ to 1, which is rather more than 333,000, so the sun is less dense than the earth. It compares roughly with that of Jupiter; its density relative to water is 1·41. Here, then, we have the dimensions of an average star.

The next point of interest is its surface temperature. By allowing the sunshine to fall on a suitable physical apparatus it is possible to determine how much radiant heat per square centimetre per minute is received by the earth's surface. Correcting for heat absorbed by the atmosphere, this 'solar constant' comes to 1·93 calories. The calorie is a small unit of heat used in physics; in terms of the gas or electricity bill, $2·5 \times 10^7$ calories make a therm and $8·6 \times 10^5$ an electrical unit. What a calorie can actually do is raise 1 gm. of water through 1° Centigrade (which is 1°·8 Fahrenheit). Now the intensity of radiation varies inversely as the square of the distance, so from the experimental 1·93 the radiation rate at the sun's surface can be calculated. But the rate of emission for a perfect radiator is directly proportional to the fourth power of the temperature. Thus, and confirmed in other ways, the temperature of the sun's surface is known to be about 6,000°C. The interior is very much hotter, but a discussion of this will be deferred until the last chapter.

When the sun is examined with a telescope* we see the white disk called the photosphere. It does not seem quite so bright around the edge, or limb, on account of our oblique view. We are looking down into the sun's atmosphere and can see through it only for a certain distance; this limited distance will lead to a deeper and hotter layer in the centre of the disk, where the line of sight is normal to the surface, than near the edge where it is not. This darkening of the limb is much more apparent in a photograph than in visual observation. The surface itself has a granular 'rice pudding' appearance. The granulations, which are a few hundred miles across, are in constant movement and may be the tops of masses of hot gas rising from the lower levels. In all probability some spots will be visible (Plate VIII, p. 129), black markings that come and go; they may last for days or weeks, and if they do they are likely to change their shape and, quite often, their relative position. Day by day observations of these spots show that the sun rotates on its axis, and, like Jupiter, not all at the same rate. At the equator the period is about 25 days, but in the polar regions 34 days. As seen from the earth the periods will be a little longer, for our planet is moving around the sun in the same direction as the rotation. Spots are never very far from the equator, within 35° of latitude north or south, and assuming that it

* Do *not* try to do this without proper equipment; it is dangerous.

lasts long enough, a given spot would be seen to take just about four weeks to go right around.

Before studying a photograph of a sunspot consider a few simple diagrams, Fig. 37. In A the two parts of a

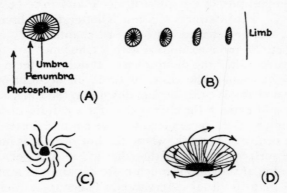

Fig. 37. The nature of a sunspot

spot are shown, the dark umbra and the less dark penumbra. When a spot is near the limb, B, it is foreshortened, so that we see less penumbra on one side and more on the other; thus the spot is a funnel-like depression in the sun's surface. Photographs taken in hydrogen light with the spectroheliograph (page 74) sometimes show filaments of hydrogen as illustrated in C. In conclusion, then, a sunspot appears to be something in the nature of a whirlpool of rising gases, D. Since they are rising they are moving to a region of lower pressure and must therefore expand, and just as compression causes a rise in temperature, expansion is accompanied by a fall. The spots are not really dark; they are emitting a lot of light, but being at a lower temperature they are less bright than

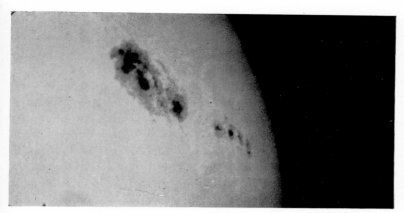

A great sunspot, 1946, Feb. 9.   *Greenwich Observatory*

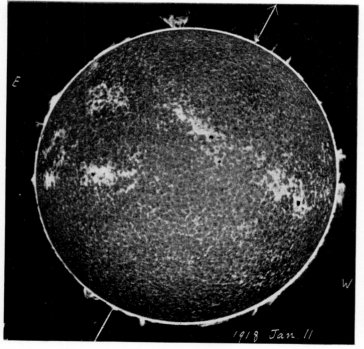

The sun in calcium light, 1918, Jan. 11.   *Evershed*

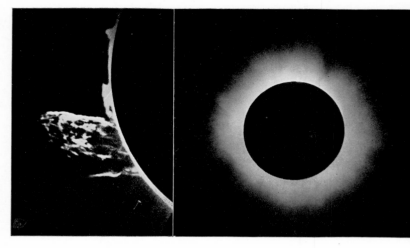

A solar prominence, 1916, May 26
Evershed

The solar corona, 1926, Jan. 14
Aston

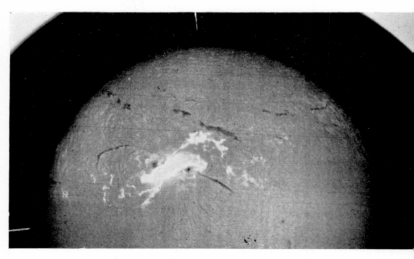

A great solar flare, 1946, July 25
Observatoire de Meudon

the surrounding photosphere and therefore look dark to us. Single spots are quite common, but they often occur in pairs, and a large pair may be accompanied by numerous small spots making an impressive group. There are also magnetic fields associated with spots, but for the method of detection of this magnetism the reader must turn to one of the more advanced books on astronomy. Plate IX (p. 144) shows an abnormally large group of spots; it was one of the largest on record, though even it was exceeded the following year by the group shown in Plate VIII (p. 129). The spot area in IX is about 5,000 millionths of the sun's hemisphere and the whole length of the group is 200,000 miles; the earth on the same scale as the picture would be 0·08 inch in diameter.

This photograph also shows associated with the spots a considerable area of surface of abnormal brightness. These patches, which are not always limited to the vicinity of spots, are called 'faculae' and are best seen when near the limb. Also occurring in disturbed areas are short-lived eruptions called 'flares' (Plate X, opposite). They are watched with the spectrohelioscope and the whole affair may be over in half an hour. The gases in the flare are not only abnormally hot and bright, but are in violent motion from and to the surface beneath. Some consequences of flares will be mentioned a little later on. Pictures made with the spectroheliograph* show these features, and the faculae show up well when calcium light is used. They also show masses of calcium vapour called 'flocculi' floating above the surface (Plate IX); for non-chemists it should be mentioned that calcium is the metallic constituent of chalk but as a free metal is used only for technical, as distinct from household, purposes. Hydrogen photographs

* Called spectroheliograms.

show flocculi of this element also, but they are less prominent.

The spectrum of the sun was mentioned briefly in Ch. III, and it was there pointed out that if light of mixed wavelengths passed through an incandescent vapour of a lower temperature than the source, certain wavelengths would be absorbed and dark lines would appear in the otherwise continuous spectrum. The vapour was, of course, radiating the same wavelengths, but at a lower temperature, and not necessarily in the original direction. At the time of a total eclipse of the sun the disk of the photosphere is gradually covered. Just before totality a

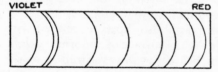

Fig. 38.   The flash spectrum

narrow bright crescent is left, and if viewed with a prism the crescent will itself act as a slit and produce a spectrum like Fig. 38. Fraunhofer's lines are there, but are curved because the spectrum is made up of images of the surviving bright crescent. When the photosphere is completely covered the continuous background goes out (like switching off the lamp in the experiment on page 70), and for a brief interval the curved lines form a bright line spectrum. This 'flash spectrum' is due to the light of the 'reversing layer', where the absorption responsible for Fraunhofer's lines takes place; the duration of the flash spectrum gives an indication of the thickness of this layer—a few hundred miles, but merging gradually into the next layer.

This outer layer is called the chromosphere, and is seen
as a ring around the totally eclipsed sun. This too is in
constant movement and gives rise to prominences, Plate
X (p. 145) top left, vast masses of luminous gas, such as
hydrogen, reaching perhaps 100,000 miles or more from
the sun. Some are quiescent and remain for some time;
others are eruptive, changing almost from moment to
moment. A trick with a spectroscope has long enabled
them to be seen without waiting for an eclipse, and there
is now an even more efficient device called a Lyot filter.
A number of beautiful cinema films have been made,
showing prominences rising up and dying down, or rising
in one place and arching over to fall at another, or rising
high above the chromosphere with incredible velocities
and detaching themselves altogether. There is certainly a
vast field of ever-changing study in the sun! Needless to
say, prominences are not confined to the limb of the sun,
but that is where they are most spectacular. When on
the main disk their motion to or from the observer enables
them to be picked out with the spectrohelioscope, and
they can sometimes be seen as black streaks on spectroheliograms, particularly the hydrogen ones.* The spectrum of the chromosphere does not contain all the
Fraunhofer lines. Of the 92 chemical elements about 60
show evidence of their presence in the reversing layer.
Most of these are also found in the chromosphere, but
owing to the difference in temperature and pressure there
are differences in spectral detail, such as the intensities
of the lines. It is interesting to remember that years
before helium, a light gas used for filling airships, had
been discovered on earth, it had been identified as a new

* One or two can be detected in the lower photograph in Plate X,
which is a hydrogen spectroheliogram.

element in the solar chromosphere and had been given its name.

Beyond the chromosphere, and also shown in eclipse photographs (Plate X, top right), is the corona, a pearly white light of doubtful composition. Its spectrum shows a faint continuous band of colour, presumably due to sunlight scattered by minute particles as in the zodiacal light, and some bright lines that were for many years unidentified and the hypothetical element was given the name coronium. Ionisation, which is a partial breaking down of atoms, appears to provide an explanation and the coronium lines have been given identities, but that has raised the difficult problem of how the degree of ionisation required can occur so far from the sun, for the corona may extend for a million miles. Until comparatively recently the corona could be studied only during eclipses, for otherwise light scattered by our atmosphere completely obliterates it. For a few years, however, apparatus designed by Lyot at the Pic du Midi Observatory, 9,000 feet up the Pyrenees, has overcome the difficulty, and perhaps more continuous study will wrest from the corona the secret of its constitution.

The spottedness of the sun may seem a matter of chance, but if records of spots be examined for a period of time a definite cycle of changes will be apparent. Sometimes the sun is seen without spots; in 1944 there were 157 days when it was in this condition. There had been 48 such days in the previous year and only 14 in the next. The year 1944 was at a time of sunspot minimum, after which there was an increase, notable for the large groups shown in our plates. The 1947 group was the larger of the two and the largest ever photographed. That year also provided the highest average sunspot frequency for many years. There was another sharp rise in 1948, but the former year is regarded as the period of sunspot maximum, and sunspot activity is slowly dying down again. Fig. 39 shows the 'spottedness' over a period of years and the general idea of this 11 year cycle can be gathered from

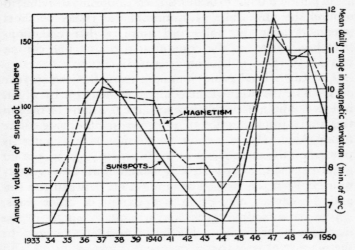

Fig. 39. The sunspot and magnetic cycles

that. Maxima do not occur with mechanical regularity and 11 years is an average period. Another feature of the cycle is the changing latitude of the spots which, it should be remembered, are confined to the zone 35° north and south of the equator. As the number of spots is dying away those that there are tend to be near the equator, but when the increase begins the spots are in the higher latitudes. At this time, of course, there may be spots in both places, the last of the old cycle and the first of the new. The prominences show a somewhat similar distribution change, becoming nearer the equator as maximum approaches, but in this case there are two zones of activity well clear of the sunspot belt and prominences here follow different eleven-year rules. The corona is also subject to the sunspot cycle. At the maximum period it tends to be more or less uniformly distributed around the sun, while at minimum there may be short streamers near the poles and some ray-like extensions stretching out from the equatorial regions. The corona in Plate X (p. 145) is of an intermediate type.

The earth itself is not immune from the eleven-year cycle. The variation of the compass is the angle by which it does not point true north, and there is a daily change in this angle, just a fraction of a degree on either side of the mean value. If the average magnitude of this change is plotted on the same paper as the sunspots (Fig. 39, dotted graph) the similarity is striking—there must be a connection between the two. The connection between the sun and the earth's magnetism is apparent in other ways. There are sometimes large and irregular changes in the magnetic measurements, known as magnetic storms. In the maximum year 1947 there were 19 major storms, and in 13 cases they occurred when a fairly large spot was not far from the central meridian of the sun's disk, suggesting that something projected from the spot in our direction was responsible for the storm. There is reason to believe that the flares are the real culprits; let us take a specific instance (1). On May 21, 1948 at 11.19 a.m., a flare was observed 70° off the central meridian, maximum development being estimated at 11.24. At 11.20 there was a slight tremor in the magnetic record, at 11.23 solar noise was heard on appropriate radio receivers, and at 11.25 there was a fade-out in short-wave long-range transmission. All these events occurring at this time cannot be a series of coincidences, and note that whatever is disturbing the magnetism reaches us with the speed of light. In the earth's upper atmosphere, where the pressures are low, there is considerable ionisation giving what could be described as electrified layers, the ionosphere. It is believed that a flare sends out a powerful burst of ultra-violet radiation, which is an ionising agent and increases the electrification of the layers at from 50 to 60 miles in altitude. This change in electrification causes the changes in magnetism. Now long distance radio is only possible because radio waves travel up from the earth's surface and are then reflected around the curvature of the globe by these very layers. The enhanced ionisation causes the layers to absorb short waves instead of reflecting them, and hence reception fades. Long wave transmission is also affected, but in this case it takes the form of increased interference from stray noises known as 'atmospherics'. Solar noise is a direct transmission from the sun on radio wavelengths; a little more will be said about this when we have completed the consideration of flares. Take another case (2). Flare observed (from the daylight part of the globe of course) at 02.30 G.M.T. on January 23, 1949, at a point only 5° from the centre of the sun's disk, and ionospheric disturbances were noticed at both 02.00 and 03.00; apparatus for observing solar noise was not available. On the 24th at 18.28 G.M.T., 40 hours after the flare, there was a great magnetic storm, and at 18.50 a display of the Aurora or Northern Lights began. Here it seems there must be something that takes a considerable time to get here, and the phenomena are attributed to electrically charged particles arriving to alter the state of the upper atmosphere. The Aurora (3) is a display of

coloured lights high in the atmosphere over the earth's
poles, where the lines of magnetic force are concentrated
vertically. It is a common and wonderful phenomenon
in the polar regions, and occasionally a great display like
this one (4) can be well seen all over this country and be of
general interest to the public. This corpuscular emission
seems to have directional properties, for with the former
flare, 70° off our direction, there was no storm. The flare
of February 1, 1949 gave the immediate results on magnetic records and radio, and 38 hours later there was a
mild magnetic storm; the flare was 51° off the meridian
and the beam nearly missed us.

The reception of radio waves from a non-terrestrial
source is nothing new; the apparent correlation between
sunspot frequency, short-wave fadeout and this hissing
noise had been noticed in 1936. In 1942 the army radar
on 4 to 6 metres was being disturbed in this way and Hey
investigated the difficulty (5). With directional apparatus
he found that the effect was coming from the direction of
the sun, on which there was a large spot. The great spot
of 1946 gave opportunity for a detailed investigation, and
by 1947 the source could be localised to within about 10
minutes of arc and to the actual region of the spot. The
noise intensity is not constant, but it does seem to depend
on the size of the spot, the bigger the spot the greater the
noise, and to fall off rapidly when the spot leaves the
central meridian. This is high level noise; some solar
noise goes on all the time, even when there are no spots.
Flares produce large bursts, but they are not so directional
as those from spots. The radio telescope (Plate III, p. 96)
is a parabolic mirror of wire netting which, like an optical
telescope, reflects and concentrates the incoming radiation
to the focus, at which the receiver is placed.

Sunspots are blamed, without justification, for many things. The weather, for instance, though it must be obvious that you cannot blame a sunspot because it is raining at the seaside when it happens to be fine at home! Investigations on sunspots and the weather are inconclusive. There seems to be a long term effect on climate though; when an old tree is felled the rings of growth in the trunk are revealed, and a study of the thickness of these rings shows an eleven-year cycle. Eleven-year cycles have been sought in all sorts of things, such as rabbit population and the briskness of business on Wall Street! They hardly justify description here, where we have a limited number of pages for the whole universe, but very readable information is available (6).

The Distance and Brightness of Stars

One star has now been dealt with in considerable detail; it remains to attack the rest, and the problem of their distance comes first. Readers will remember that the parallax of the sun is the angle subtended at the sun by the radius of the earth. For the distant stars a larger base is needed, and thus the parallax of a star is the angle subtended by the radius of the earth's orbit, i.e. by one astronomical unit. Stellar parallax is so small that it was unmeasurable until 1838, when three independent observers, using different apparatus and different stars, met with some success. In Fig. 40 S represents a star which is very much nearer than the other stars in the same field, and D one of the very distant background, so that E_1D and E_2D can be taken as parallel. Then as the earth moves around in its orbit the star S, here drawn in the plane of the ecliptic, will oscillate to and fro among the fainter and distant stars (see inset). If this displacement x, greatly exaggerated in the diagrams, can be measured, it gives the angle at the star subtended by the earth's movement in the interval, or in this case, twice the parallax. If the star S were at the pole of the ecliptic its parallactic annual motion would be a circle instead of a line, and in any intermediate position an ellipse. Originally the distance between the

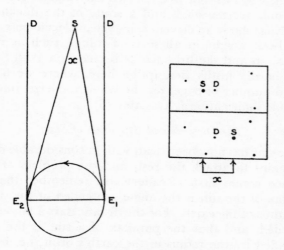

Fig. 40. The parallax of a star

stars S and D had to be measured with instruments on the telescope, and as no parallax yet found is as great as one second of arc (you will remember from page 45 how small that is) the measurement is not easy. The modern method is to photograph the star field when the earth is at E_1, E_2 and E_1 again, and measure the positions of the images on the plates. Knowing the parallax the distance of the star can be calculated in astronomical units or miles, though neither of these units is really big enough. The astronomer's unit is the 'parsec', the distance of a star having a parallax of 1 second; if the parallax were 0".1, the distance would be 10 parsecs. The popular unit is the 'light year', or the distance light travels in one year. The velocity of light is 186,000 miles per second, and this when multiplied by the number of seconds in a year gives 6 million million miles. A parsec is rather larger, being 3.26 light years or 19.2 million million miles. Here are the results for the three stars first measured: 61 Cygni, 1838, by Bessel; α Centauri, 1839, by Henderson; Vega (or α Lyrae), 1840, by Struve:

Star	PARALLAX		DISTANCE		
	Original	Modern	Parsecs	Light-years	Miles
61 Cygni	0.314	0.300	3.33	10.9	64×10^{12}
α Centauri	1.0	0.758	1.32	4.3	25.3×10^{12}
Vega	0.262	0.124	8.06	26.3	155×10^{12}

For all practical purposes α Centauri can be regarded as the nearest star so far discovered, though it has a near companion below naked eye visibility which is very slightly nearer and is called Proxima.

α Centauri and Vega are bright stars and may therefore be expected to be among the nearer ones; the former turned out to be a good choice. But why choose 61 Cygni, only just visible to the naked eye? That was quite a good choice too. The so-called fixed stars are not fixed at all, and if accurate star catalogues differing in date by a good many years be compared, the 'proper motions' can be deduced. The comparison of photographs is, of course, the modern method. These are not real motions, but apparent and relative. In Fig. 41 let the sun be at rest and the star moving in the direction SA, the length of SA being proportional to the annual change in real position. This can be divided into SB, across the line of sight and called the proper motion, and SC in the line of sight and measurable with the spectroscope (see p. 72). If the star were at rest and the sun moving in the direction of the dotted arrow the same results would be found, and it is very likely that both are moving. Then of course there is the annual parallax cycle due to the earth's motion as

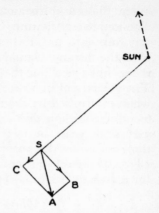

Fig. 41. The proper motion of a star

well, so disentangling the apparent motion of a star is a serious business. Now on an average we may expect a large proper motion to indicate a near star. Imagine that you are on a cricket ground, in the stand with binoculars. It is the lunch interval, and boys of all ages from eight to 80 are prowling about the ground to look at the wicket. Here you have moving objects with some variety in velocity and great variety in distance and direction. If a figure moves rapidly across the field of view of your glasses it is almost certain to be someone on your side of the ground. Now proper motions are not large. Only about 50 stars exceed 2″ a year; 61 Cygni has a motion of 5″·2 and α Centauri 3″·7. Hence their fortunate choice for the first distance determinations. This direct method of finding the distance of a star is limited to the nearer stars, say up to 160 light years. Indirect ways will be mentioned later and details can be found in other books (7), but several thousand distances have been determined in this trigonometrical manner, and that gives us quite enough to go on with.

The system of classifying stars in magnitudes was explained in Ch. III. If stars differ by n magnitudes, the light received from them is in the ratio $2 \cdot 512^n$; five magnitudes give a light ratio of 100. What we are more concerned with in this chapter is the light emitted by the star, rather than that received by our photometer, and this depends upon distance. The apparent brightness of a source varies inversely as the square of the distance, so if its distance be known we can calculate what it would look like at some other distance. For the purpose of comparing stars we calculate what their magnitude would be if they were situated at a distance of 10 parsecs, or $32 \cdot 6$ light years, and this is called the absolute magnitude. Thus if 61 Cygni, which can be taken for the present as having a magnitude of $5 \cdot 6$, were moved out from $3 \cdot 3$ parsecs to 10, it would then appear to be of magnitude $8 \cdot 0$. The brightest star in the sky is Sirius, mag. $-1 \cdot 58$, but that is a comparatively near star and would become much more ordinary when pushed out to 10 parsecs. The second brightest, Canopus, is more interesting, for it shines at mag. $-0 \cdot 86$ in spite of its immense distance. There is some doubt as to what its small parallax really is, comparatively recent measures varying from $0'' \cdot 005$ to $0'' \cdot 028$. Taking $0'' \cdot 014$, the distance becomes 71 parsecs or 232 light years, and if this star were brought in to the standard distance it would brighten up to $-5 \cdot 4$. If the sun were similarly treated its magnitude of $-26 \cdot 7$ would dwindle to $+4 \cdot 8$. To compare the light emitted by these two stars with that of the sun, the rule $2 \cdot 52^n$ must be applied, and for 61 Cygni n is $8 \cdot 0 - 4 \cdot 8 = 3 \cdot 2$ in favour of the sun. Thus the luminosity of 61 Cygni is $\frac{1}{19}$ of that of the sun. Applying the rule to Canopus that star turns out to be over 12,000 times more luminous than our own. We have already noted the great range in magnitudes of the stars as we see them, giving a ratio of over $10^8 : 1$ between average bright stars and the faintest seen in our telescopes; there is evidently a considerable range in real luminosities too!

Mention was also made in Ch. III of the fact that magnitudes determined by visual and photographic methods differ on account of the colour of the stars; a reddish star might be bright to the eye and faint to the camera. The difference photographic minus visual is known as the colour index of the star, and for white stars it is zero and for red ones over a magnitude. The colour index is related to the spectral class (see next section), so if the spectrum has been studied and the photographic magnitude found, the visual magnitude can be calculated. On the other hand a determination of magnitude by both methods will give an indication of the spectral class.

The Character of a Star

First, its colour. Some people deny that the stars have colour, because by colour they expect vivid contrasts like traffic lights or railway signals. A careful observer, however, is conscious of delicate variations in tint, such as when the red Betelgeuse is compared with the bluish-white of the neighbouring belt of Orion. If two different coloured stars can be viewed in the same telescopic field the contrast is even more obvious and sometimes very beautiful. The colour gives a clue to temperature. Everyone is familiar with the expressions 'red hot' and 'white hot'. When the temperature of, say, a lump of iron is gradually raised it begins to radiate, at first only with long infra-red wavelengths. As the temperature gets higher, shorter and shorter wavelengths are included in its emission until the visible part of the spectrum is reached, beginning with the red—the iron is now glowing at red heat. When the

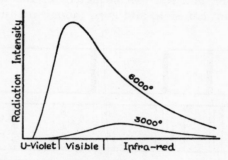

Fig. 42. The distribution of energy in a spectrum

temperature rises still further other wavelengths are added and the light appears whiter. Fig. 42 shows the distribution of energy in the spectra of perfect radiators (called by physicists full radiators or perfectly black bodies!) at 3,000° and 6,000° respectively. Note that the peak of the lower temperature one is in the infra-red, and although all visible wavelengths are included there is more energy in the red end and the object would be emitting reddish light. The peak of the 6,000° graph is at half the wavelength of the other and is in the visible part; there is a law that the wavelength of maximum radiation is inversely proportional to the absolute temperature. Absolute temperature is a scale of Centigrade degrees starting from absolute zero, the temperature at which a body contains no heat energy at all, and is expressed as degrees K. As absolute zero is − 273°C, the absolute temperature of a body is its Centigrade temperature plus 273. Absolute temperatures are implied in the rest of this book; that need not be a complication as it differs from Centigrade by only a very small fraction of a stellar temperature. Now the spectrum of a star can be tested for the wavelength of maximum emission, and even though it is not quite a

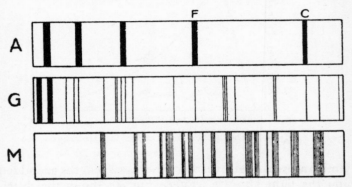

Fig. 43. Stellar spectra: A, a very hot star; G, a star like the sun; M, a cool star

full radiator the temperature can be estimated with fair accuracy. Notice also in Fig. 42 how much greater is the area under the 6,000°K curve; it represents the total radiation, which is directly proportional to the fourth power of the temperature. This method of estimating temperatures was described in the case of the sun and can be applied to stars also.

The spectrum of the sun has already been considered, and it is that of an average star; those of many of the others look quite different. Fig. 43 is purely diagrammatic and does not show, by far, all the Fraunhofer lines; more detailed representations can be found in the text books (8), (9). They represent what catches the attention when using simple apparatus: A is for a star much hotter than the sun—a few bold lines; G similar to sun—many fine lines; M much cooler than the sun—rather indefinite bands. The nature of the spectrum is, of course, linked with the temperature, and in the following brief account of the Harvard types we will take the hottest first.

Type B, approx. 20,000°: Fraunhofer's lines, mainly of helium and hydrogen, two very simple elements. The colour of the star would be bluish-white.

Type A, approx. 10,000°: The helium lines have vanished but the hydrogen lines have become very strong and bold. Colour: white.

Type F, approx. 7,000°: The hydrogen lines are still strong, but lines due to the metals are becoming noticeable, particularly calcium. Colour: yellowish white.

Type G, approx. 5,500°: There are now many metallic lines and the hydrogen no longer stands out. The calcium lines called K and H, in the deep violet, are very bold (one has almost the same wavelength as a bold hydrogen line in Type A). With lower temperature there are more complex atoms present. Colour: yellow.

Type K, approx. 4,000°: Like the last, but with less prominent hydrogen and more prominent metallic lines. Colour: orange.

Type M, approx. 3,000°: The striking feature this time is the appearance of broad bands, sharp on the violet side and fading out on the other. The temperature is now low enough for chemical compounds to exist, and

L

the prominent bands are due to titanium oxide. Colour: red.

In addition to these there are several other types of a rather special nature, some including bright lines and one, Type O, applying to a temperature of 40,000°. To cover the gradual transition from type to type a decimal sub-division is used. Thus B9 is nearly like an A star, and K5 is half way between K and M—in fact bands are just detectable in K5.

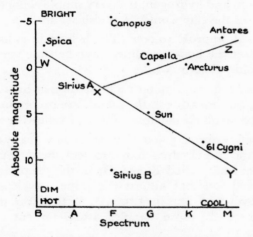

Fig. 44.   The Russell diagram relating luminosity and spectrum

This, then, is the system. If a spectrum can be photo-graphed and classified it gives another pointer to tem-perature and tells us something of the chemical constitu-tion.

In the early part of the century it was noticed that in the case of the red stars they were either very bright or very faint, with nothing in between. A red star, it seemed, could have an absolute magnitude brighter than -1 or fainter than $+9$, so such stars fall into two classes, one about 10,000 times as luminous as the other. Since their surfaces are at the same temperature one must have a lot more surface than the other, and this led to the titles giants and dwarfs. This distinction is not, however, confined to red stars, as shown by the very interesting Russell diagram, Fig. 44. Here spectral type is shown horizontally and absolute magnitude vertically, and it is found that a considerable proportion of the several thousand points that can be included are spread reasonably near the diagonal line WXY. A considerable number also lie along the branch XZ, though this time with rather wider scattering, particularly in the band G to K. XZ represents the giant series and XY the dwarfs; it is more usual, however, to call the whole of WY the main sequence. There are some stars that do not fit on either branch. Canopus and a few other well-known ones are of very high luminosity and are white; these are known as supergiants. There are also some white stars of very low luminosity, of which Sirius B is an example; these are the white dwarfs. There are not very many samples of them, because stars of such low luminosity could not be seen unless comparatively near to us, which the specimens available are. Two other points about the Russell diagram. It suggested a theory of stellar evolution: a star began life as a red giant and finished as a red dwarf. The giant, a sphere of low density, contracted under its own gravitation, and as the material 'fell' towards the centre of gravity, potential energy due to its position was lost and heat energy, more than enough to provide for emitted radiation, took its place. Thus the star became hotter and smaller, and its position in the diagram moved down ZX. When this gravitational energy had been used up, continued radiation could only result in a fall in temperature, so the star slipped down XY to a red dwarf and to extinction as a cold 'black dwarf'. The other point is that although the spectral type of two stars, such as the sun and Capella, may be the same, the relative intensities of the lines may differ. The spectrum of Capella is not quite the same as that of the sun, for the former star is a dozen times as big and 100 times more luminous—the spectrum does show whether the star belongs to the giant or main sequence series. Consider a star too distant for a parallax measurement but bright enough to study the spectrum. Suppose it is type G. The spectral lines will indicate whether it is a giant G of absolute magnitude 0·0 or a dwarf G of 5·0, and having thus got an estimate of the absolute magnitude this need only be applied to the apparent magnitude in the sky and the distance of the star has been found.

A star is too distant to present a discernible disk in the telescope, and thus a direct observation of its diameter is impossible. A few of the larger stars have been measured with an instrument called an interferometer attached to the Mount Wilson 100 inch reflector. This is a 20 foot girder with a mirror at each end and two near the middle; light from the star is collected in two beams about 20 feet apart and reflected down the telescope tube. To explain just how the two wave trains interfere and provide an answer to the problem would involve yet another long digression into physics (10); let us accept the fact that it does. The diameter can also be inferred from the magnitude and the spectrum—the energy distribution in the spectrum gives temperature, the radiation laws enable surface brightness to be found from this, and by comparing this estimate with the observed brightness the area of the surface (in square seconds of arc) can be found. In the case of the directly measurable stars, the angular diameter (the largest of which is only 0″·04) estimated in this way

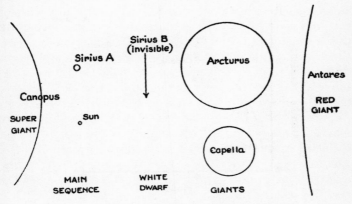

Fig. 45. Some well-known stars drawn to scale

is in close agreement with the measurements, and thus we may reasonably use the method for stars not directly measurable. There is a very wide range in stellar diameters: that of a very large star, Antares, is 320 times the sun's; on the other hand the white dwarf called Van Maanan's star is only the size of the earth. This gives a range of 35,000 to 1. A few well-known stars are drawn to scale in Fig. 45.

To anticipate a little, quite a number of stars consist of two components revolving around a common centre of gravity like the earth-moon system. If it is possible to determine fully the details of the orbits, then an application of Kepler's third law enables the combined mass of the system to be calculated in terms of the sun as unity.* In some cases the individual masses of the components can be found. On an average the mass of such a pair is 2·2 times the sun's, and the masses of stars in general lie

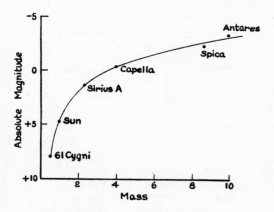

Fig. 46. The mass-luminosity diagram

between 0·1 and 10·0 times the sun's with, of course, an occasional exception. It has been found that if masses and luminosities, where both are known, be suitably plotted, they lie quite close to the line shown in Fig. 46. This is called the mass-luminosity law, discovered by Eddington. Only binary stars are available for direct mass determinations, but there is no reason to suppose that the mass-luminosity law applies only to them. Thus we can use the law to find the masses of any stars of

* The law on page 34 can be expressed in the form $M = R^3/T^2$, where M is the combined mass in terms of the sun, R the radius of the orbit in astronomical units and T the period of revolution in years.

which the absolute magnitude is known, excluding white dwarfs.

The range in masses, then, is about 100 to 1; the range in diameters was no less than 35,000 to 1. Density is equal to mass divided by volume, and volume is proportional to the cube of the radius. Hence the variation in density is simply enormous, more like a million to one. Stars of the main sequence have densities comparable with that of the sun; highly luminous stars near the top of Fig. 44 are larger than the sun, but also heavier. The giants, on the other hand, must be very tenuous indeed, that of an average red giant being about $\frac{1}{100000}$ relative to water, which is a very good vacuum from a terrestrial point of view. However, a vacuum is a familiar thing; the high density of a white dwarf is more difficult to understand. The mass of Sirius B, for instance, is nearly equal to that of the sun, but in size it is comparable with the planet Uranus. This gives the incredible density of not less than 35,000; a cubic inch weighs 11 cwt., and Sirius B is not the densest star. The heaviest known element has a density of under 20; how can 35,000 be achieved? A long deferred digression must now be undertaken to find the answer.

Until comparatively recent times all matter was considered to be built up of two kinds of particle, the proton and the electron. Several new fundamental particles have been discovered, but only one, the neutron, need be mentioned here. The proton possesses one unit of mass and one unit of positive electric charge. The neutron has one unit of mass but no charge. The electron has one unit of negative charge and a mass extremely small in comparison with the proton. A lump of material, let us say chalk, consists of molecules, each containing a certain number of atoms which in this case would be of the elements calcium, carbon, oxygen. The molecule is the unit of chemical compounds, and by chemical processes such as heat it can be broken down into its constituent atoms. The atom consists of a positively charged nucleus of protons and neutrons, and the whole is made electrically neutral by electrons circulating in a series of shells outside the nucleus. The simplest atom of all is hydrogen and it consists of one proton and one electron. The next is helium with a nucleus containing two protons and two neutrons, giving it an 'atomic weight' of 4; to maintain neutrality there are two circulating electrons, giving an 'atomic number' of 2. Incidentally the helium nucleus is also known as an 'alpha particle'. Lithium has an atomic weight of 7 and atomic number 3, and so on. Of heavier elements sodium has 11 protons and 12 neutrons in the nucleus and 11 electrons outside, 2 in an innermost shell, 8 in the next, and a lonely one in the third. The chemical properties are determined by the electrons in the outermost shell, so it is not surprising that some similarity in properties occur between lithium and sodium, Fig. 47, each having one in the outermost shell. If, now, an atom loses or gains an electron it will be no longer a neutral atom but a charged ion, positive in the former case and negative in the latter, and its properties will change in some respects. There are various factors

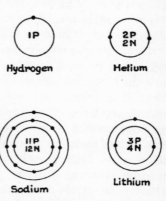

Fig. 47. The structure of the atom

that can bring about ionisation, a very relevant one from an astronomical point of view being the impact of ultra-violet light (e.g. in the corona, page 148, and in the ionosphere, page 151). At high temperatures ionisation by collision is important. The formation of spectral lines is presumed to be due to the sudden transfer of electrons from one orbit to another, and we should therefore expect to find a change if the element concerned has lost one or more of them. Spectral lines due to ionised elements are quite common. Type O stars show ionised helium and doubly ionised (i.e. two electrons gone) oxygen; in the cooler A stars there is neutral helium and singly ionised oxygen. The H and K solar lines are due to ionised calcium.

The atom has often been described as a miniature solar system. The analogy is rather far-fetched, for the planetary orbits lie in fixed planes and the planets do not leap about from orbit to orbit. In one great respect they are alike; they both occupy a space out of all proportion to the quantity of matter contained. The radius of the planetary system is 3,666 millions of miles; most of its mass is concentrated in the sun. Cut off the three outermost planets, corresponding to a trebly ionised atom, and the radius is reduced to one quarter. Remove all the planets and the mass of the system is reduced by only 0·1 %, but the radius is reduced to less than one million miles, to $\frac{1}{4000}$ of what it was. Ordinary neutral atoms, then, cannot be packed more closely than we normally find in dense solids; strip them of their electrons and they can be packed to the density of a white dwarf. The high temperature of a stellar interior, millions of degrees, is presumed responsible for this drastic ionisation.

One other problem: Do the stars rotate? The sun does,

and we may reasonably expect the others to do so too. With the sun or a planet the Doppler shift can be used to measure rotation, for if the slit be directed to the receding edge of the disk the lines will be displaced towards the red, and for the approaching edge towards the violet. We cannot do this with a star, for all the light enters the spectroscope at once, but if the star is rotating fast enough the displacements will be there and we shall see both at once—making the lines look wider than they should. Such widened lines have been found and rotational velocities deduced from them.

In reading this section it should be noted how much the astronomer is dependent upon piecing together odd scraps of apparently disconnected information. On an average it serves him very well and quantities deduced from one set of data usually agree with those otherwise obtained. Sometimes a weak link lets him down and they don't, but when numbers are large 'on an average' is more reliable than would at first sight seem possible. We will conclude this section by putting in tabular form the characters of several stars (page 172). The standard of accuracy is not, of course, as high as that of the planet table in the last chapter, and in some cases the figure quoted is the author's choice from differing authorities, but it will give some idea of the wonderful variety of the stars.

Special Stars

The middle star of the handle of the Plough, if carefully examined with the naked eye, is seen to be two stars, Mizar the brighter and Alcor* the fainter. There are quite a number of naked eye pairs like this, and others that are not quite so, but are divided easily with low

* Not shown separately on the map.

power binoculars. In cases of this kind the stars may or may not be physically connected. They may be merely accidentally in almost the same line of sight; a common proper motion and parallax would provide evidence of a link between them. If this pair be examined with a telescope Mizar itself is seen to be double, stars of magnitudes 2·1 and 4·2 lying 14″ apart. There are a great many telescopic double stars and they, like Jupiter's satellites, are a great joy to beginners with a telescope. To mention only a few, our old acquaintance 61 Cygni is rather like Mizar, only wider; β Cygni is one of the sights of the heavens, a 3rd magnitude yellow star with a 5·3 blue in attendance. γ Andromedae is another but closer yellow and blue pair, with the added interest that the lesser star is itself double, its components being about 0″·38 apart and revolving around one another in 55 years. Pairs with a relative motion like this are called binary stars and are normally the closer ones; the trouble with wide ones is that their periods would be too long to be readily detected. Some binaries are too close for the telescope to separate at all, but their duplicity is revealed by the spectroscope. One of the components of Mizar is a spectroscopic binary. The plane of their orbits points more or less in our direction, so at one stage A is coming towards us and B going away from us, and the Doppler effect shifts the spectral lines of A towards the blue and of B towards the red. When they are moving across our line of sight there will be no shift at all and the two sets will be superimposed. Thus the lines in the spectrum of this star are alternately single and double. This is an almost ideal case; in many, owing to the inclination of the plane of the orbit or to wide differences between the components, the changes are more complicated and difficult to unravel.

THE VARIETY

Class of Star	Name	Magnitude	Parallax (seconds)	Distance (light-years)	Absolute Magnitude	Spectrum*
Red Giant	Antares	1·22	0·014	230	−3·3	Mo
Super-giant	Canopus	−0·86	0·014	230	−5·4	Fo
Giants	Arcturus	0·24	0·087	37·5	−0·3	Ko
	Capella	0·21	0·078	42·5	−0·3	Go
Main	Spica	1·21	0·017	180	−2·3	B2
sequence	Sirius A	−1·58	0·386	8·6	1·4	Ao
	Sun	−26·7	—	8 min.	4·85	Go
	61 Cygni A	5·6	0·300	10·9	8·0	K5
White dwarf	Sirius B	8·4	0·386	8·6	11·3	Fo

* Temperature and colour can be

Let us consider a binary in a little more detail. Castor is a famous telescopic one with a period of the order of 300 years, and it has been known long enough for a considerable part of its path to be drawn on paper, Fig. 48. The measurements that are made at the telescope are shown in the diagram, and it is obvious that the brighter component has been used as a point of reference and the elliptic path of the other around it has been plotted. With regard to this ellipse the brighter star is certainly not at one focus; in fact it does not look to be anywhere in

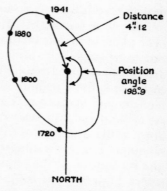

Fig. 48. The double star Castor

OF THE STARS

Diameter (miles)	Mass ($Sun=1$)	Density ($Water=1$)	Remarks
265,000,000	10	$2\cdot8\times10^{-7}$	One of the largest stars
68,000,000	12	$3\cdot3\times10^{-5}$	Second in apparent brightness; statistics very uncertain
22,000,000	4·0	$1\cdot4\times10^{-4}$	
12,000,000	4·0	$1\cdot4\times10^{-3}$	
2,800,000	8·6	0·26	
1,380,000	2·4	0·42	The apparently brightest star
864,000	1·0	1·41	
607,000	0·5	1·98	Bright component of a double star
29,000	0·96	35×10^{3}	

inferred from this column; see page 161.

particular. The reason is that this is not the real ellipse but a projection of it, and the first thing an investigator must do is to find the true plane, relative to the line of sight, in which the actual orbit lies. Then he can deal with the elements of the ellipse itself, and if the distance of the star from the earth is known the dimensions of the orbit can be converted into astronomical units (the distance marked in the figure is about 60 units) and, as indicated in the last section, the mass of the combined system calculated. The real motions have still not been found, for both stars are revolving around their common centre of gravity. If there is some convenient comparison star available, measurements of both components can be made with reference to that, so that both orbits can then be found and the individual masses calculated. To return to Castor, both components are spectroscopic binaries with periods of three and nine days. Note how short these are compared with 300 years; the distances between the components is probably of the order of a million miles, and generally speaking the smaller the distance the shorter the period. Orbits and masses can be calculated for spectroscopic binaries.

Suppose the distance of the double star is not known, but the angle of separation in seconds of arc and the period in years have been measured. Now we have seen that on an average the mass of a binary system is 2·2. Assuming that this is an average case the 2·2 can be used in the formula and the separation in astronomical units deduced. This can be compared with the separation in seconds and the parallax found—another indirect method of estimating stellar distances.

Sometimes the duplicity of a double star is difficult to see, on account of a wide difference in magnitude, a well known case being the Pole Star, 2·1 and 9·0 at 18″. Sirius is more interesting because the companion was discovered before it was seen! In Ch. IV it was explained that the earth and moon were both revolving around a point called the barycentre, and it was this point, not the earth, that was in smooth orbital motion around the sun. To an external observer the earth would appear to wobble its way along its path. Sirius has quite a large proper motion and Bessel noticed that this was a wobble too. In 1844 he concluded that there was a heavy but dim companion and that the period of the pair was about 50 years. The companion was first seen by Alvan Clark in 1862. The details of the two stars are given in the table of characters; the distance between them is about 20 units, and the maximum angular separation, 11″·5, occurred in 1925. This Sirius B is a star of interest in more ways than one, as we saw in the last section (11). And talking of wobbles, one of the stars of 61 Cygni does it, and in this case it is suspected of having a large planet of period 2 years.

Castor provided an example of a multiple star, one to the eye, two to the telescope, four to the spectroscope, and common proper motion links a neighbouring spectroscopic binary with them, making six in all. Another interesting case is ε Lyrae, Fig. 49. The slightest optical aid

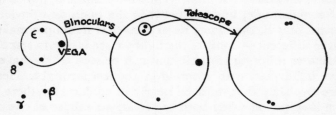

Fig. 49. The multiple star in Lyra

divides it into two, at a distance of 208″; a telescope divides each of these into two with separations of 3″ and 2½″; one of these four is a spectroscopic binary. Then there is the beautiful little trapezium in the heart of the Orion nebula—but the list is endless and there are other 'special stars' in the queue.

If the orbital plane of a binary star is parallel with the line of sight from the earth it becomes possible for one star to pass in front of the other, thus cutting off some or all of its light. Such a pair, therefore, would appear to us to vary in brightness; it would not be visible as a pair. This constitutes a variable star of the eclipsing class, and the notable example is Algol, the Devil Star, in the constellation of Perseus. It is normally a star of the 2nd magnitude, but at intervals of just under three days it falls rapidly to 3·5 and at once begins to rise again, the whole fall and rise being a matter of about 10 hours. This is a close binary star with a period of 69 hours, and once in each revolution there is a partial eclipse of star A by star B. Between these eclipses the light remains fairly steady, and the question arises 'What about eclipses of B by A?' As far as the naked eye observer is concerned the answer is 'nothing'; accurate photometry, however, shows that there is a small secondary minimum, only 0·05 of a magnitude, midway between the main and obvious ones. Star B, then must be so faint that its eclipse makes little difference—most of the light we see is due to star A. Another eclipsing variable that can be seen by the naked eye is β Lyrae, with a period of about a fortnight. Here are two stars that must be nearly in contact, for there is no long period when both are clear, an eclipse of one or other is always going on, and they themselves are probably elliptical in shape. They are unequal, for the star drops by one magnitude at one minimum and half a magnitude at the other. Rough sketches of their light curves are shown in Fig. 50. About 1,000 eclipsing variables are known.

The star δ Cephei is of quite a different class, for the variation is due to some change in the star itself. The shape of the curve is characteristic of this type, a steep rise and a slow fall, though among the type there is a wide range of periods, from hours to weeks. The spectrum of δ Cephei shows periodic changes too, indicating that at maximum brightness the surface is at a higher temperature than at minimum. Further, there are Doppler shifts showing that at maximum the surface is approaching and at minimum receding, as if the star were being blown in and out like a child's balloon. The pulsation is not quite in step with the brightness; maximum light occurs

Open cluster: The Pleiades.   Also a meteor trail.   *W. J. S. Lockyer*

Globular cluster: Omega Centauri.   *Cape Observatory*

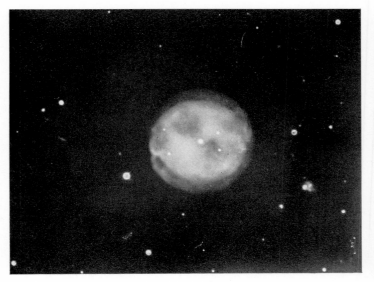

Diffuse nebula: M 42, Orion

Planetary nebula: M 97, Ursa Maior (The Owl Nebula)

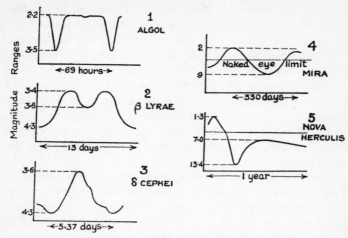

Fig. 50. Light curves of variable stars

during the blowing out process, and by the time maximum size has been reached the light has begun to fade. This luminous pulsating giant is the type star of about 2,000 variables known as Cepheids, a considerable number of which form a sub-class called cluster variables because of their location.

There is visible from the southern hemisphere a mass of stars called the Lesser Magellanic cloud, of which the distance is so great that differences in distance of one star relative to another can be neglected. It was in this cloud that Miss Leavitt discovered that for the Cepheid variables contained in it there was a numerical relationship between magnitude and period, showing a period-luminosity law, for the stars are all at one distance. Subsequently similar results were found for other clusters, establishing the phenomenon as a universal law for

M

Cepheids. Now this is very useful. From the results for the cloud a graph can be drawn but the magnitude scale will be an arbitrary one unless the distance be known. If the distance of one Cepheid can be found, its absolute magnitude can be calculated and used to fix the scale of the graph; the graph can then be used to read off the absolute magnitude, and hence the distance, of any other Cepheid whose period can be observed. A Cepheid, then, is a lighthouse out in space flashing, not its name, but its luminosity and distance—method No. 4 for fixing the scale of space.*

Some variable stars have very long periods, such as Mira the Wonderful in the constellation of Cetus. The general character of its curve is illustrated, showing it to be below naked eye visibility for a considerable part of its period, but it is less regular than those previously considered; both magnitude range and period are themselves variable. Mira is also a giant, probably pulsating, and showing complicated changes in its spectrum. Some, again, have no fixed period, an example being the red giant Betelgeuse, which varies from 1·0 to 1·4. This is one of the stars capable of having its diameter, which is larger than that of the orbit of the earth, measured directly, confirming the pulsation. It seems in this case that maximum brightness corresponds with minimum size.

A Nova, or new star, is one which appears where there was no star before, and after a brief and sometimes brilliant career fades back into obscurity. There was, of course, a star there before, faint, but visible on photographs taken before the outburst had drawn attention to the spot. The light curve of Nova Herculis (1934) is shown

* 1, Trigonometric, page 153; 2, Spectroscopic, page 164; 3, from binary stars, page 174.

in Fig. 50. This nova was first noticed by Mr. J. P. M. Prentice on December 13, just above naked eye level, and it occupied the position of a star of the 14th magnitude. By December 23 it was nearly of the 1st magnitude and well into the newspapers. It faded slowly until the end of March, when it was 4·4, and then rapidly dropped to the 13th. This behaviour was more or less normal, though perhaps more steady than some, but it was followed by another outburst, rising to magnitude 7; a second attempt is unusual but not unique. Remembering that 5 magnitudes corresponds to a light ratio of 100, the original outburst means a gain in luminosity by a factor of 120,000! The nova has since faded to and remained at the 13th magnitude. Novae in general are very distant; this one under discussion is a near one, only 750 light-years, so the original explosion really occurred in 1184! Another bright nova occurred in Puppis in 1942, reaching magnitude 0·0, but it was very short lived and was difficult to see in northern latitudes. In 1946 there was an interesting event, for Nova Coronae of 1866 had another burst, reaching magnitude 3 and lasting for a week; it was first seen by a 15-year-old boy, M. Woodman. One or two other novae have staged repeats. The brightest nova in this century was in Aquila in 1918, magnitude −0·5, and the brightest on record is Tycho's star of 1572, magnitude −4 and visible in daylight. In 1885 a nova was seen in the Andromeda nebula, which is 1,000 times more distant than Nova Herculis. It was apparently of the 6th magnitude, which at that distance means an absolute magnitude of about −15; this is 20 magnitudes more than the sun, so its luminosity must have exceeded the sun by 100 × 100 × 100 × 100! There have been others of this kind, and to them is given the name 'super-novae'. The spectrum of a nova shows remarkable changes, including bands and bright lines, and it is now thought that the central star throws out spheres of expanding gas (12). Nebulous disks have been seen around several faded novae; the 1934 object has been described quite recently as showing a greenish disk 3" in diameter, like Neptune in fact, but with a starlike point in the centre.

The remaining 'special stars' we cannot see at all! These are the radio stars, the name given to small areas of sky from which radio waves are received with much higher intensity than round about. The radio telescope is directed to the appropriate part of the sky and the rotating earth carries it round while the strength of the 'galactic noise' is measured. When a radio star passes over it the graph of signal strength rises to a sharp peak. The position cannot be pin-pointed like an optical observation, but it can be localised to within a fraction of a degree, and in most cases there is no object of special significance to the eye or camera. Important localised sources have been found in the constellations Cygnus, Taurus, Coma Berenices, Hercules and Cassiopeia (13); the original determinations of position have been used in the map. A more recent method, more analogous with the transit telescope, has given slightly different results and many more have been found (14). Their distribution is well scattered in galactic latitude, like that of the brighter and nearer stars. A system of magnitudes has also been developed; of the five quoted above the source in Cassiopeia is the strongest, magnitude − 3·4, and Hercules the weakest at +1·3.

This has been a long chapter, but unravelling the mystery of starlight cannot be hurried and the treatment has been all too short as it is.

REFERENCES

(1) Details in *The Observatory*, 68/192, 1948.

(2) *The Observatory*, 69/74, 1949.

(3) See C. M. Botley, *The Air and its Mysteries*.

(4) Photographs and notes, *Journal of the B.A.A.*, 60/23, 1949.

(5) Ch. V, reference (9). Solar noise is also well described by A. J. Higgs, 'Radio Astronomy', in *Science News No. 21* (Penguin), 1951.

(6) H. T. Stetson, *Sunspots and their Effects*, 1937.

(7) Such as F. J. Hargreaves, *The Size of the Universe*, 1948.

(8) Photographic spectra: H. Spencer Jones, *General Astronomy*, 1951.

(9) Visual spectra: with notes by P. M. Ryves, *Journal of the B.A.A.*, 59/70, 1949.

(10) See reference (8) or other more advanced book.

(11) See also W. M. Smart, *Some Famous Stars*, 1950.

(12) See reference (11); a very readable account of Novae.

(13) See Ch. V, references (9) and (11).

(14) An account of the method and a list of 50 positions north of the equator is given by Ryle and others in *Monthly Notices of R.A.S.*, 110/508, 1950.

As a brief, simple and extremely readable account of the subject matter of this chapter and next, D. S. Evans, *Frontiers of Astronomy*, 1946, can be strongly recommended.

ADDENDUM. Progress in radio astronomy has been very rapid. The number of radio sources now (1956) known is very large indeed, and considerable success has been achieved in identifying sources with optical objects such as nebulae. Radiation has been detected from Jupiter and suspected from Venus. A giant new radio telescope, 250 feet in diameter and steerable, is nearing completion at Jodrell Bank and is a prominent landmark just east of the railway line from Manchester to Crewe. References: A very useful account of this branch of astronomy is given in *Occasional Notes of R.A.S.*, No. 16, 1954, and a description of the new telescope in *Discovery*, XV/185, 1954.

CHAPTER VII

The Stellar System

Local Groupings

THE individual members of the stellar system have now been studied, and we come to the question of their distribution, which is not as random as at first sight appears. The study of proper motions shows the existence of moving clusters, and an example can be found in the familiar Plough. Except for the more northerly pointer and the end of the handle, the prominent stars have the same proper motion—they are going the same way at the same speed, companions in space. A considerable number of stars, widely scattered and including Sirius, share in this motion and the whole collection, the Ursa Major group, occupies a volume of space about 100 light years across. Our sun, and of course ourselves, are within this volume but do not belong to it. The Taurus group is more compact; its centre is 130 light years away and the 80 stars composing it lie within a radius of about 16 light years from its centre just to the west of the bright star Aldebaran. In our sky it makes a circle about 15° in diameter. If their directions of motion are plotted they are found to be not parallel but convergent, and line of sight velocities (also called radial velocities) are away from us. When a group of aircraft abreast fly overhead on parallel courses they don't look parallel once the group has actually passed; their courses converge to a vanishing point in the distance. Similarly these Taurus stars have their vanishing point, just to the east of Betelgeuse. There are several other moving clusters besides these.

The Taurus group does at least look like a cluster; a gathering of stars in a small region is quite obvious. The densest part of it is the Hyades and is an example of an open cluster. Not far away lie the Pleiades, compact enough to be seen together in the field of binoculars, and one of the prettiest views in the northern heavens (Plate XI, p. 176). They are popularly known as the Seven Sisters, though only six stars are readily noticed with the naked eye; binoculars bring the number up to 20 or 30. Another open cluster resolvable with binoculars is Praesepe, M44*; this is smaller and less bright than the Pleiades and to the unaided eye is only a hazy spot. Between Cassiopeia and Perseus, in the Milky Way, is a bright spot marked on star maps as X (chi) Persei. This is smaller again and is not so easy to resolve, but quite a small telescope shows it to be two more or less circular clusters just touching one another. There are some 300 of the open clusters, many of them, however, being purely telescope objects. They lie not very far from the galactic plane, i.e. the plane of which the Milky Way forms the edge, and distributed fairly evenly all round.

The next class of object is the globular clusters, of which the northern showpiece is M13 in Hercules. Whether or not it is visible to the naked eye is a matter of opinion; with good sight and a clear moonless night, perhaps it is, and it is usually regarded as such. A small instrument shows a hazy spot, and it needs quite a large telescope to resolve it properly. The example illustrated in Plate XI is one of the southern showpieces, ω (omega) Centauri, and the justification for the name globular is obvious.

* No. 44 in Messier's catalogue.

Cepheid variables can be identified in some of these clusters and that enables their distances to be estimated, that of M13 being about 30,000 light years. At this distance its diameter of 18' would be equivalent to 150 light years, though the dense central zone would be less than this. The number of stars is large, probably not under 100,000, but nevertheless they are really quite well spaced out. If we were placed in the central regions of one of these, quite a number of stars would be as near or nearer than Proxima, and there would be more very bright ones, but we should still have room to make our annual journey around the sun without any extra perturbation. From the clusters containing Cepheids it appears that they are of approximately uniform size, and assuming this to be the general rule the apparent size can be used as another means of distance estimations. The nearest, 47 Toucani, is at about 25,000 light years—much the same as the farthest open cluster—and the farthest a little under 200,000. Their distribution in the sky, as will be shown later, is of some significance. They avoid the galactic equator by some 10° on either side, and are largely concentrated into one half of the star sphere. This class of cluster numbers about 90.

We now leave the globular clusters and move on to the planetary nebulae, so called because when seen in a telescope they are disk-like, similar to planets. Most of them are small, not more than 1' in angular diameter, though M97, shown in Plate XII (p. 177) and known as the Owl Nebula, is considerably larger. The diffused disk, which frequently, as in this case, shows some kind of detail, has a star at the centre. The highly tenuous sphere of matter around it may to some extent be reflected light, but it is much more probable that it is being stimulated into self-radiation by the strong ultra-violet emission from the star; there is little doubt that the central star is the responsible party. Such stars are of very high temperature but low luminosity, an indication of white dwarf status. Some planetary nebulae are in ring form, there being a well-known example (M57) in Lyra, and we have already noted that novae throw off shells of matter and tend to surround themselves with nebulous disks. These nebulae may, therefore, represent former novae, though admittedly some of them seem rather large to have so originated. Distances range from 1,500 to 50,000 light years; radii are more uniform at about 10,000 astronomical units (1). In distribution they favour the plane of the Milky Way, which was avoided by the globulars, but like the latter show a concentration towards the zone of the sky lying between galactic longitudes 270-360°.

Of the diffuse nebulae the outstanding example is M42, illustrated in Plate XII. It is a pity not to be original; this picture has appeared so many times before but it simply cannot be missed. The object is visible as a hazy spot just below Orion's belt and is worth examination with any optical aid. It does not look like the picture, but if anything more beautiful. The nebulosity is a transparent greenish veil through which the stars, including the multiple star called the Trapezium, shine clearly. The spectrum shows bright lines, as would be expected of re-radiation stimulated by the ultra-violet of the embedded stars. Some of the lines were long unidentified, and were given the name Nebulium Lines, but they are now known to be due to ionised oxygen and nitrogen. With longer exposures the photographs show more nebulosity, and almost the whole constellation is covered. This is a not uncommon phenomenon, and another example occurs in the Pleiades.   Here the enveloping nebulosity gives a dark line spectrum, suggesting that its light is due to reflection. Diffuse nebulae are numerous but these two examples must suffice.   M42 is 980 light years away and 14 light years across; the corresponding numbers for the Pleiades are 500 and 50.

We have seen, then, the gaseous nebulae, vast volumes of matter of exceedingly low density, emitting light directly or indirectly in consequence of embedded stars.   What if there were nothing to bring about this emission? Study Plate XII again. Note how in certain places the luminous veil ends suddenly and gives way to an intense blackness. This certainly suggests an obstructing mass of non-luminous gas, a dark nebula, and there are many examples of it, some being more striking than this one.   On a larger scale there are dark patches in the Milky Way, a famous one being the Coal Sack in the Southern Cross (Crux) area.   An obstruction of this kind can be seen in Plate XIII (p. 192) upper.   At one time they were thought to be 'holes in the heavens', tunnels through the stars giving a glimpse of black empty space beyond, but it is far more likely to be due to the dark nebulae.

The spiral nebulae, mentioned in Ch. II as Lord Rosse's milestone, are a numerous class of quite a different kind. The greatest distance so far mentioned in this chapter is 200,000 light years; the nearest of this new group is nearly a million and for some of them hundreds of millions. The discussion of these, therefore, will be left until we come to the section 'Beyond the Milky Way'.

This will be a convenient point to mention the motion of the sun. If you are travelling down a long lighted street as exemplified by some of our arterial roads, the lamps ahead are seen to be opening out and those behind closing in.

When the proper motions of the brighter and nearer stars were studied the same effect was found. In one direction, in the constellation of Hercules, the stars were opening out; this point is called the apex of the sun's way. There is a similar point, the antapex in Columba, to which the stars are closing in. Thus the motion of the sun, with a velocity of 12·5 miles per second, is revealed and has since been confirmed by measurements of radial velocities. This motion, it must be understood, is relative to the nearer stars only and can be regarded as the sun's random motion in space.

The Galaxy

The name Galaxy, was formerly, and sometimes still is, used as an alternative name for the Milky Way. It is more usual now to use the word as a collective name for the star system to which we belong, together with everything we can see except the very distant extra-galactic nebulae. The name will be so used here, and the pale luminous band across our sky will keep its familiar title of the Milky Way.

This band, the integrated light of myriads of faint and distant stars, is very nearly a great circle about the star sphere, though we do not see the whole of it at once and in the latitude of England there is a part that we never see at all. It varies considerably in width and brightness, the brightest part being in the neighbourhood of Sagittarius, galactic longitude 320-330°. The galactic equator, about which the Milky Way lies, is shown in the map; longitudes, so important for stellar studies, are measured eastward along it from its intersection with the celestial equator in Aquila. The poles of the galaxy, galactic latitudes +90° and −90°, are also marked. For about one third of its length, roughly from longitude 290° to 50°, the starry band is divided into two streams.

That, then, is what we see; how can we explain it? One explanation is that there is a genuine ring of distant stars, and the sun lies close to the plane of the ring. If we imagine, for the present, that the varying brightness of stars is due mainly to their distance, a more satisfying

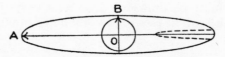

Fig. 51.   A possible distribution of the stars

explanation presents itself. Suppose that the stars were uniformly distributed in a disk-like volume shown in cross section in Fig. 51, and that we, the observers, were near the centre O. It is obvious that we can see more stars in the direction OA, in the plane of the disk, than in OB, for the simple reason that it is the direction of greatest depth, providing more stars to see. Many of them would be distant stars, and therefore, faint, too faint, in fact, to see as individuals. The individual naked eye stars would be the near ones, say within the circle about O, and these would be more or less equally distributed all around us. Thus we should have a roughly equal distribution of stars, and a ring of indistinct starlight marking the plane of the disk. Sir William Herschel was interested in this theory and sought supporting evidence by counting the number of stars he could see with one of his telescopes when pointed in various directions. Then assuming that the greater the number, the further he could see, the shape of the star system could be inferred. Herschel's diagram was not so

symmetrical as Fig. 51, but the general idea was the same.
To account for the divided third of the Milky Way, he
supposed that there was a rift or cleft on its edge, indicated
by the dotted line. We now know that Herschel's telescope
was insufficient to penetrate to the edge of the system,
though its range would be larger than the circle shown.

A modern statistical survey was made by Kapteyn in
1922, but, unlike Herschel, he had available the photographic magnitudes of the stars in his selected areas, and
he counted, not the total number, but the number of each
magnitude. When changing from one magnitude to the
next the average brightness would be less by the factor $2\frac{1}{2}$
and, assuming this to be due to distance alone, the average
distance would be greater by about $1\frac{1}{2}$, for the brightness
varies inversely as the square of the distance. In Fig. 52
AOB represents the angle of the area under observation
and the circles are drawn so that each is $1\frac{1}{2}$ times as big

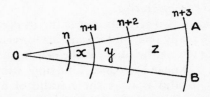

Fig. 52. The increase in number with decreasing brightness

as the preceding one. In changing from magnitude n to
$n+1$ we count the stars in x, for the next magnitude the
stars in y, and so on. If the stars were uniformly distributed there would be an increase in the number each
time and this increase can be calculated. The most important result of Kapteyn's work was that the rate of
increase was a diminishing one; the stars are not uniformly

distributed, but diminish in number the further we go. The rate of falling off increased as the observations moved away from the plane of the Milky Way, suggesting a lens-shaped distribution. There was little change in different galactic longitudes, suggesting that the observer was near the middle.

When discussing the globular clusters it was mentioned that their distances could be measured, and a remark was added about their distribution. This enabled Shapley to make another and dimensioned model of the stellar system; it turned out to be an ellipsoidal volume, rather like a thick teacake, 150,000 light years in diameter with its greatest dimension in the plane of the Milky Way. The clusters are equally divided north and south of the galactic plane, so the observer is situated near that plane; they are largely in one half of the sky, so the observer must be well out towards the edge. Shapley estimated that the centre of his system was about 50,000 light years away from us in the direction of Sagittarius.

Thus we have two systems coexisting in the same space but probably really one, and it remains to reconcile them, for according to one the sun is at the centre and according to the other it is near the edge. One suggestion is that the sun belongs to and is near the middle of a local lens-shaped cluster, the members of which are masking the large-scale distribution beyond.

We have already noted the existence of obscuring matter in space. These patches are more numerous in the galactic plane, and the Milky Way is divided for a part of its length including both Shapley's centre and the brightest part in Sagittarius. The star population is greater near the centre of the system, and it is reasonable to suppose that the density of the inter-stellar dust would be too.

This state of affairs is illustrated in the drawing in Plate XIII (p. 192). The Milky Way will be richer in the region ABC than in CDA, and ABC is also where it will be divided by obscuration. This plane of dust will also obscure the distant globular clusters, which, as we have seen, do not occur within 10° of the galactic plane, but not the much nearer planetaries. It will explain too why Herschel and Kapteyn did not discover that OB was greater than OD. A lighted street was mentioned a few pages back; if there was fog you would see which way the street ran, but you would not know how far along you were because the lamps would thin out equally both ways. There is other evidence for the existence of this inter-stellar dust. Certain lines in the spectra of distant stars indicate absorption not in the atmosphere of the star but in the intervening space. Some distant stars are redder than would be expected from their spectral class, just as a lamp is reddish when shining through fog. Photographs taken in red light show more stars than when taken in blue, for red is more penetrating, as was mentioned in connection with the atmospheres of the planets.

Red light is more penetrating among fine particles because it has a longer wavelength. Radio waves are very much longer, and should therefore penetrate the inter-stellar dust almost unimpeded. Radio stars were mentioned in the last chapter as localised sources where the galactic noise is more intense than its general level. This 'general level' has been investigated and mapped, and is found to rise rapidly as the Milky Way region is approached. The maximum occurs in the direction of— well, you can guess the rest, it is in Sagittarius, the direction of the supposed galactic centre where there would be more matter to radiate than in any other direction. Thus radio gives another and supporting indication that the theory of the galactic centre is right.

Estimates have been made of the effect of absorption by inter-stellar dust on the observed magnitudes. As an indication of the kind of result it may be mentioned that the estimates range from 0·7 to 1·1 magnitudes per 1,000 parsecs, that is to say stars 1,000 parsecs away would be about 1 magnitude brighter if the obscuring dust wasn't there; this refers to the galactic plane region. Making allowances of this nature the star counting was repeated by Van Rhijn and Bok. It will be remembered that Kapteyn's results were that the density of star population in space decreased outward from the sun in all directions, whereas there should have been an increase towards Shapley's galactic centre. The trouble was, of course, that it was just in this direction where there were more stars to count that there was also the greatest obscuration. The new results showed that there was a decrease, at first, in this critical direction, but it was followed by the expected increase. This supports the idea of a local cluster, and in fact these investigators found evidence to show that it was another ellipsoidal volume 5,000 light years in diameter, with its centre in the direction of Carina and its plane inclined at 12° to that of the galactic equator. It has been suggested that the sun's motion towards Hercules is a rotation within this local cluster. On the other hand, as will be shown later, there is a very strong reason for doubting the real existence of this local cluster.

The next problem is that of the rotation of the galaxy, not as a wheel but as an enlarged solar system. There is no central sun; the centre of rotation would be the centre of gravity of the whole system as for a pair of binary stars. The further out from the centre a star is situated the

Milky Way in Ophiuchus
Lick Observatory Photograph

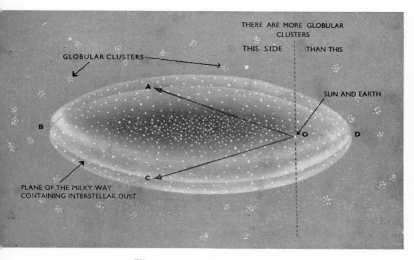

The structure of the Galaxy
Discovery

Spiral nebula: M 31, Andromeda
Yerkes Observatory

Greater Magellanic Cloud
Franklin-Adams

slower it moves, and this loss of velocity with distance can be deduced from a study of radial velocities. A difficulty, one which has occurred before, is that of separating systematic motions from random ones, so let us return to the cricket ground for a while (page 156). The initial rush to the wicket is over; the old boys are wandering about smoking their pipes and the young ones are chasing tennis balls; all are just killing time until the bell goes to clear the ground for the resumption of play. If it were possible to measure the direction and velocity of each person and work out the mean value it would come to zero. If a sufficiently large number of people are going nowhere in particular, then on an average (with apologies for using this expression again—it does convey an important idea) they are not going at all. Repeat the experiment at the close of play when once more hundreds of people are scurrying or ambling hither and thither. This time the average is not zero, for superimposed on the random motions there is a systematic one, toward the exit. Similarly, if in a given direction the mean radial velocity of a sufficiently large number of stars is determined, the result will be the systematic relative velocity between them and the observer—the random movements will have been eliminated.

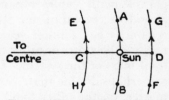

Fig. 53. The relative motion of the sun and its neighbours due to galactic rotation

Fig. 53 shows the orbit of the sun, together with an inner and an outer orbit. The stars A and B will have no motion relative to the sun, for their orbit and period will be the same. C is overtaking the sun and D getting left behind, but while they are in the positions shown they are

at a constant distance, so that radial velocities are zero.
E and F are increasing their distance because the former
is getting ahead of the sun and the latter being left behind;
there will be radial velocities of recession. Similarly G
and H are getting nearer and show velocities of approach.
This distribution of radial velocities can be detected; they
confirm the direction of the centre, and indicate that
orbital velocities decrease by 1 mile per sec. for an increase
in distance of about 400 light years, quite enough to
scatter a local cluster. These results are of course based on
observations of large groups of stars, not individuals. If
the actual velocity of the sun in its orbit could be found
we could then deduce the radius. The solar motion previously discussed was relative to nearer stars, to those
probably sharing almost the same galactic orbit. When
more distant objects like globular clusters are used as the
frame of reference, different and much higher velocities
are found, the generally accepted value at present being
170 miles per second in the direction of Cygnus. The
corresponding radius, though less than Shapley's, is comparable with values obtained by other means and the
period of revolution for the sun, and stars in the same
region, is 225 million years. Knowing the velocity and
radius it becomes possible, as with double stars, to find the
total mass of the system. This is of the order of 10^{11} suns,
or perhaps double that. Some of it is not stars but diffuse
matter; on the other hand quite a lot of stars are lighter
than the sun. This same number, then, one or two hundred thousand million, will give a fairly good indication
of the total number of stars in the galactic system. Fig. 54
has been drawn to summarise our conclusions about the
galaxy and can be left to speak for itself. It represents a
cross section perpendicular to the plane of the Milky Way,

with the north galactic pole at the top; for dimensions of the hypothetical local cluster see page 192. The sun is slightly on the north side of the central plane, for the line of the Milky Way is 1° south of the corresponding great circle on the celestial sphere (2).

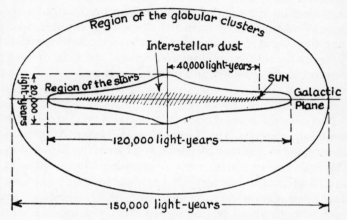

Fig. 54. Cross-section of the galactic system

One last point in this section is the phenomenon called star streaming, known since 1904. The motion of the sun through space, 13 miles per second towards the solar apex, would give the stars an apparent motion the other way. Thus we should expect the nearer stars to show a systematic motion, or, if you like, a preference for one particular direction. They were found to have two. Investigation indicated that the quick moving stars formed two streams in approximately opposite directions. The discovery of the rotation of the galaxy provides a possible explanation, for these streams are approximately to and from the galactic centre. The orbits of the solar system vary from the near-circles of the great planets to the elongated orbits of the comets and meteors, so why not the same in the galactic system? Refer back to Fig. 36 (page 132) and imagine that you are somewhere near but not beyond the aphelion end. Then the comet or meteors, when in your neighbourhood, would show one of two preferential directions of motion, to or from the sun. Thus it seems likely that the star streams are due to stars circulating around the galactic centre, in elongated orbits, crossing the sun's path on their outward and inward passages.

Beyond the Milky Way

Not very far from the south celestial pole there are two luminous patches, the Greater and Lesser Magellanic Clouds, looking rather like detached bits of the Milky Way. They are not, of course, but are in galactic latitudes − 33° and − 44°. One has already been mentioned in connection with Cepheid variables, and their distances are known, both about 80,000 light years*, the smaller being slightly more distant. Taking the diameter of the galaxy as 120,000 light years, the distance from the eccentrically placed sun to the edge in the direction of the clouds would be about 50,000. These objects, then, lie outside our system, though only just outside and are often regarded as satellite systems. Their diameters are 15,000 and 12,000 light years, and they contain the same kind of objects as the galaxy, including the most luminous known star and the greatest diffuse nebula. They are classed as irregular extra-galactic nebulae, though of course they can be seen to be star clouds (Plate XIV, p. 193). The Doppler effect shows that they are moving away from us at quite high speeds, but this is more apparent than real

*See addendum on page 203.

and seems to be tangential with the edge of the galaxy and associated in some way with its rotation.

In general the extra-galactic nebulae are much farther off, only a few being nearer than a million light years. They are divided into two main classes, elliptical and spiral; the latter are subdivided, though that need not concern us here. Plate XIV shows a large spiral with, as a satellite, a small elliptical nearby. The elliptical group vary from circular to nearly flat and are mainly nebulous in appearance. They may be disk-like objects seen from various angles, though at least some are probably spherical. The spirals explain themselves, and these can be seen from various angles, as shown in Plate XIV and the frontispiece. To a considerable degree, particularly in their outer parts, they can be resolved into stars, and they can be arranged into a sequence of increasing openness and resolution. Sir James Jeans regarded this sequence (3) as evolutionary, the spherical unresolved type at the beginning and the Magellanic Clouds at the end. His theory was that the nebula began by a gathering of interstellar matter into a spherical clump which was somehow set into rotation. Rotation caused flattening, first into an ellipsoid, then into a disk, and finally into a spiral. At the same time the gaseous mass gradually condensed into stars, just as a cloud of steam condenses into water droplets, and a star cloud was the final stage. Not everyone now agrees with this evolution. The similarity of the later forms of these island universes with our own galaxy is striking and to some extent confirms the theory of galactic structure outlined in the last section. We see our own only from the inside, but we can get external views from all angles of others like it, and the edge-on nebula in the frontispiece is remarkably like Fig. 54.

The presence of Cepheid variables in the nearer extra-galactic nebulae enables their distances to be found. The study of these objects of known distance shows that the brightest stars are of approximately the same absolute magnitude, about -6, in all of them. This gives a method of estimating the distances of objects not containing Cepheids, for the apparent magnitude can be measured and the -6 assumed. The next step is the study of the brightness of the nebulae as a whole, and this shows, for those of known distance, that the average absolute magnitude is -15. Thus the apparent magnitude of a nebula not resolvable into stars can be used to estimate the distance.

The two nearest great spirals are M31 in Andromeda and M33 in Triangulum, both probably between 700,000 and 800,000 light years away. M31 is the larger, with a diameter of 40,000 light years, and is just visible to the naked eye; it is the most distant object discernible to unaided sight. A helpful analogy was given by Jeans, who likened the galaxy and these two to London, Oxford and Cambridge. Their sizes, distances and, taking people as stars, populations were in just about the right proportions. He wrote over 20 years ago; we now believe that our own star city is not so large in comparison with the others, and M33 is considerably smaller than M31. There are also a few smaller 'towns' of non-spiral type not so far away as these two.

The Andromeda nebula resembles the galaxy in a number of ways. Its shape is probably similar. The outer parts are well resolved in photographs taken with great telescopes and enable its content to be examined. There are clusters, a few of the open type and many globular, gas clouds and variable stars. It is well supplied with giants and super-giants, and several novae have been seen, including the great super-nova mentioned on page 179. Line of sight velocities found with the spectroscope show that one edge is receding and the other approaching, so this object is rotating. By observing nearer the centre of the system, it is found that, as we should expect, the inner parts are moving quicker; values quoted for one revolution of objects near the middle is 11 million years, and near the edge 92 million. The spectroscope also gives a hint of which edge is the nearer; the photograph does not tell us whether we are looking at the north or south face of the nebula. We have seen how galactic obscuration causes a reddening of distant stars; stars on one side of the oval image of the nebula seem to be slightly redder, and therefore more distant, than on the other. Measurements of internal velocities of the nebula should make it possible to find the total mass of it. Another approach to the problem is to estimate how many suns would be needed to produce the known absolute magnitude, and then add a bit on for other forms of matter. Results vary very widely, but are of the order of 10^{10}—but might well be ten times more or less than this. This M31 is a particularly large and near specimen of its class, and is naturally fairly well known, but quite extensive knowledge has been derived for a number of others.

The number of extra-galactic nebulae is very, very large. It is believed that at least two million are already within telescopic reach, and there may be millions more which, on account of distance or small size, are not yet detectable. They are scattered about the sky in all directions, though not seen in the region of the galactic equator for obvious reasons. They are, however, frequently found in clusters, our own galaxy belonging to a small one. This local gathering includes our satellite systems (the Magellanic Clouds), M31 with its satellites (M32 and another), M33, and some half a dozen minor ones. As the galaxy is at one end and M31 and M33 at the other, this family of islands will be about 800,000 light years across. The nearest major cluster, in the constellation of Virgo, is seven million light years distant and is slightly larger but more densely populated, for a diameter of a little over a million light years contains two or three hundred nebulae. This is very crowded! It is estimated (1) that for the whole of space so far explored the average distance between two nebulae is 1,730,000 light years. The distance explored is assumed to be 500 million light years; the Palomar telescope should double it. Some 20 odd clusters are known with distances up to about 250 million light years, but there are probably many more, and the numbers of nebulae in each range from a few hundred to 2,000 or more; this does not include numerous small groups like the local one. Taking 500 million light years as our range of visibility, imagine that the visible universe was a sphere the size of the earth with the sun at its centre. This would give a scale of half an inch to the light year. The galaxy would be a disk nearly a mile in diameter; Proxima Centauri would be two inches from the sun; the diameter of the solar system to the orbit of Pluto would be about $\frac{1}{1500}$ of an inch; the size of the earth would be—insignificant to say the most of it. The extra-galactic nebulae (often called the other galaxies) would, as far as we know, be smaller than a mile, but supposing there were three million of them they would have about 90,000 cubic miles of space each. How much the universe contains, and yet how empty it is!

The spectrum of an extra-galactic nebula is similar to

that of a star, a dark line spectrum, but naturally it is faint and not very distinct. Fortunately the K and H lines (see page 161), being very bold, are identifiable even in faint specimens and can be used to study radial velocities. The results are astonishing; nearly all the objects are moving away with very high speeds. Fig. 55 is a sketch showing what the spectrum looks like; the upper part is a com-

Fig. 55.   Spectrum of an apparently receding nebula

parison spectrum of helium and the lower that of the nebula, little more than a smear of light. The two gaps in this smear are the K and H lines (not included in the Helium spectrum), shifted quite a long way towards the red end of the spectrum. Assuming this shift to be due to the Doppler effect it means a velocity of recession of over 12,000 miles a second! The Andromeda nebula shows a velocity approach of 190 miles a second, but this can be accounted for by the rotation of the galaxy. The nearest major group, in Virgo, at a distance of seven million light years, is receding at about 560 m.p.s.; the example in Fig. 55 (in the Leo group) is at a distance of 100 million light years; the highest velocity available at the time of writing is 38,000 m.p.s. for a nebula 360 million light years distant. Notice that the further the faster. A law has been deduced from these, for the velocity increases by 100 m.p.s. for each million light years of extra distance, and gives us a spectroscopic means of measuring nebular distances. The last example represents the limit of equipment formerly available, but Dr. Humason, who has been working on this for years, now has the use of the new Palomar instruments and hopes to extend the distance-velocity law by 50% (4). This question of recession will be taken up again in the next chapter.

Attempts have been made to detect radio emission from the extra-galactic nebulae, and naturally the large and near M31 was the first subject of research. Radiation from this nebula had been suspected for some time, but not confirmed until 1950 when the Jodrell Bank team definitely obtained results. The radio telescope was 218 feet in diameter, made of wires at 8 inch spacing supported by concentric rings of posts of various heights; it was a gigantic spider's web, in fact, but parabolic in shape. The receiver was supported at the focus, 126 feet up, by a mast that could be tilted up to 15° so that it can be made fully effective in directions other than quite vertical. A continuous record of power received was kept at the appropriate time, and as M31 was carried past by the rotation of the earth the intensity rose (5). A radio star gives a sharp peak in the intensity graph, but the nebula, being an object of finite width, gave a more rounded maximum. The intensity obtained was only a small fraction of that of a radio star. Radiation from other near nebulae has been detected with apparatus at Cambridge (6).

REFERENCES

(1) Readers interested in stellar statistics should see P. Doig, *Outline of Stellar Astronomy*, 1947.
(2) A standard work on this section is B. J. and P. F. Bok, *The Milky Way*, 1944.

(3) See pictures in J. H. Jeans, *The Stars in their Courses*, 1931.
(4) A short note on this Palomar programme is given in *Discovery*, XII/236, 1951.
(5) See Ch. V, Ref. 11, and R. Hanbury Brown in *Journal of B.A.A.*, 61/180, 1951.
(6) See Ch. VI, Ref. 14.

Readers who would rather follow up this radio work in a book should see B. Lovell and J. A. Clegg, *Radio Astronomy*, published at the end of 1951. It is a students' book, technical in places.

ADDENDUM. Just after this book was printed in 1952 Dr. Baade reached an important conclusion as a result of his work with the 200 inch telescope. Mention was made on p. 177 of the division of the Cepheid variables into two groups, and it is now known that they do not obey quite the same period-luminosity relationship. Distances, such as the size of the Galaxy, depending on the cluster type are still valid, but the other, or " classical ", Cepheids are brighter and more distant than was thought. Thus all extra-galactic distances mentioned in this book should now be doubled. Another consequence is that the short time scale (p. 226) should also be doubled. References: The original announcement appears in *Transactions of the I.A.U.*, VIII/397, 1954. Popular accounts will be found in *Sky and Telescope*, XII/238, 1953, and *Discovery*, XV/20, 1954.

CHAPTER VIII

Mysteries still Unsolved

THIS is a controversial chapter, both in the choice of topics and in their treatment; the author is in the unhappy position that 'anything he says may be used in evidence against him.' Hitherto we have confined our study to ascertained facts, and to those theories upon which there is wide agreement. Now one or two problems will be stated, together with some brief account of various ideas that have been put forward to solve them.

Stellar Energy

This is a great fundamental problem. There is a law in physics, called the Conservation of Energy, which states that energy cannot be created or destroyed, but only changed in form. We have seen that the sun is delivering energy to the earth at the rate of 1·93 calories per sq. cm. per minute. To deliver this quantity upon an object 93 millions of miles away means that the sun's output must be many horse-power over every square inch of its surface. Countless millions of stars are doing much the same thing, and the total quantity of energy being poured out into space in the form of radiation is almost beyond human comprehension. Whence does it come? A variety of sources have been suggested, mainly with reference to the sun but, of course, applicable to other stars as well.

A hint as to one source was given on page 163. When a body is suspended above the surface of the earth it is capable of falling, and in falling of doing mechanical work. It is possessed of potential energy, and if it is allowed to move nearer to the centre of gravity of the earth, the body of which it really forms a part, that energy must be converted into another form. This idea can be applied to a star, for if a diffuse one were to contract, its individual parts would be 'falling', towards their common centre of gravity and an energy conversion going on. A red giant, then, may contract into an ordinary giant, and further into a star of the main sequence, and as it does so its temperature would rise and maintain the star in its right place in the Russell diagram. When this argument is applied to the sun it is possible to deduce for how long the supply would last, and the answer is 20 million years. There is fair agreement about the age of the earth, which cannot be greater than that of the sun, and this is between 2,000 and 4,000 million years. Thus although gravitational energy may be one source it cannot be the only or main one, and a search must be made for another.

What about meteors? Everyone has seen the shooting star and knows that heat is being produced, and we also know that meteors are very numerous. If a body were to fall from infinity to the sun it would acquire a velocity of about 400 miles a second, and as the energy of its fall is proportional to the square of the velocity it will be large. Quite promising so far. From the rate of emission of energy the rate of arrival of meteors can be calculated, and this leads to the fact that the sun would in consequence double its mass in about 30 million years—an unlikely event to say the least of it, and meteoric bombardment can be dismissed.

Towards the end of the last century Radioactivity was discovered. This is the spontaneous disintegration of certain heavy atoms, of which radium and uranium have already been mentioned, with the liberation of considerable amounts of energy. Here was another possibility for the source of the sun's energy; the presence of these elements in the sun could account for its present radiation rate, but could not keep it going for the necessary millions of years. The time scale required defeats this method as conclusively as the other two.

The law of conservation of energy has already been mentioned. There is also a law, used in chemistry, of conservation of matter. Einstein has shown that these two laws are really one; instead of 'energy = a constant' and 'mass = a constant' we have the one law 'energy + mass = a constant'. Thus the interchange between the two becomes possible, and the relation is $E = mc^2$, or energy = mass × the square of the velocity of light. As c is a very large number (186,000 miles per sec. or 3×10^{10} cm. per sec.) a great quantity of energy can be liberated at the cost of a very small mass*. Applying this formula to the sun's known emission of energy, that body must be losing mass at a rate of about 4 million tons a second! This sounds a lot, but 4×10^6 is a very small fraction of the total of 2×10^{27} and this rate could carry on for any length of time that we are likely to require. It can be shown that when a star is very massive it would lose mass very quickly, and then as it became less massive the rate would slow down. Thus very massive stars are scarce—their life is too short for many to be about at one time—and the majority of the stars are quietly sliding down the main sequence, having started from W or from Z (Fig. 44), as formerly suggested. This evolutionary theory is now in doubt—there is a school of thought that sends stars up the sequence instead.

* If m = 1 gram, E would be 9×10^{20} ergs.

The total annihilation of matter—existing one instant and gone the next—implied above is difficult to explain, but a partial change which would produce enough energy for the sun to shine for a long enough period has been worked out in some detail by Bethe and others. The atomic weight of hydrogen is 1·008, and that of helium almost exactly 4·0. If, therefore, four hydrogen atoms were converted into one of helium there would be a small loss in mass and a corresponding and quite large liberation of energy. This involves a change in the nuclei of the atoms concerned, but nuclear changes are not unfamiliar, as radioactivity involves their natural occurrence and the atomic pile and atomic bomb provide man-made examples. The hydrogen-helium reaction does not take place under terrestrial conditions, but it can at the temperature of about 20 million degrees which is believed to exist in the interior of the sun. Nuclear transformations in the laboratory depend upon the bombardment of complete atoms with fast moving projectiles such as neutrons, and direct hits on the nucleus are relatively few. In the stellar interior the nucleus has been stripped of its protective screen of planetary electrons (see p. 169) and is itself likely to be moving with projectile velocity (p. 99). It is tempting to describe the chain of 'thermonuclear' reactions by which hydrogen becomes helium, but it would be rather out of place in this book (1); it must suffice to say that they depend on the presence of carbon. Although the carbon takes part in the chain of changes, which involve also the temporary existence of nitrogen and oxygen, it is regenerated at the end. It therefore acts as what the chemist calls a catalyst and remains constant in quantity; the reaction can go on as long as the hydrogen supply lasts. A curious consequence is that as helium accumulates in the star it tends to keep the heat in, like clouds over the earth's surface. Thus the temperature of the interior rises, the reactions are accelerated, more energy is produced, and the star becomes generally hotter and more luminous.

These are high temperature reactions. For stars at lower temperatures others have been proposed, but these, though they also lead to the production of helium, involve the destruction of the light elements lithium, beryllium and boron. Compared with hydrogen these elements are less abundant and there is therefore a shorter time limit on the low temperature (a million degrees!) reactions. The evolution of a star now becomes something like this: A mass of gas of low density contracts under its own gravitation and a rise in temperature results. The low temperature thermonuclear reactions then begin, and we have a red star of slowly rising temperature until the light elements have been exhausted. There is then a further contraction until the temperature is high enough for the carbon cycle to begin. This stage lasts for a long time, during which the star becomes more luminous, i.e. it ascends the main sequence. When the hydrogen is exhausted there is a further contraction and the star enters its last phase as a white dwarf.

It is probably safe to say that at the time of writing the foregoing thermonuclear explanation is the current one, but an alternative source of stellar energy has been brought to the public eye through the medium of wireless talks and an exhibit at the Festival of Britain. The theory of Lyttleton and Hoyle (2) does not exclude the nuclear transformations but is supplementary to them, and is popularly called 'tunnelling through interstellar gas'. The existence of interstellar matter has already been discussed, and the new proposal is that a star gathers to it through gravitation the matter in its neighbourhood, thus adding to its energy and mass. The outer parts of the solar corona are presumed to be visible evidence of this infalling of matter. As the star moves through space it will leave behind a tunnel empty of matter; if the motion is slow and/or the interstellar matter is dense the gain in energy in this way would be considerable.

There is also an alternative theory of the red giants (2). This supposes that when a star has nearly exhausted its hydrogen content and helium is accumulating near the central regions, the non-uniformity of its composition causes it to swell, so that the former main-sequence star becomes a red giant instead of collapsing into a white dwarf as stated a page or two back. How confusing for the lay reader—but then he was warned at the beginning of the chapter that we were embarking on uncertainties.

Before leaving this topic of stellar energy some brief reference to variable stars and novae would be desirable. A steady star is in a state of equilibrium. This term, in physics, means that the various conditions affecting a body have so adjusted themselves that the state of the body remains unchanged. Take a homely example, a controlled gas cooker. At the outset the heat production is larger than the losses, the temperature rises, and the thermostat gradually lowers the gas supply. Finally, at some temperature chosen by the operator, equilibrium is reached and the heat production is equal to the heat loss. If the equilibrium is disturbed, say by rotating the control to a higher number, the temperature will rise. This causes the rate of loss of heat to rise and in time a new state of equilibrium will be established. In some cases there will not be another possible equilibrium state, and the result

o

of the disturbance will be the collapse of the system concerned. When the heat supply to the aforementioned oven increases there may not be a new state of equilibrium for the pudding inside, but a catastrophe—it boils over!

These two types of equilibrium seem to occur among the stars. A star has a tendency to collapse under its own gravitation, but this is balanced by the outward force of radiation pressure. Suppose one of these, say the latter, be reduced, then the star will contract. This contraction will cause a rise in temperature and a corresponding rise in radiation pressure. If the changes were very slow we should expect a new equilibrium to be established at a smaller size, but there is the possibility that the radiation pressure would increase too much and cause the star to expand again. Perhaps this is what happens in a pulsating variable star.

Now consider the case where radiation pressure drops suddenly, as would occur with the sudden exhaustion of the hydrogen fuel for the Bethe reactions. The sudden collapse that followed would release energy so rapidly that there would be a catastrophic outburst before the star relapsed into the white dwarf state. The reader should, however, regard this theory as an illustrative example rather than a true story; if the balance between gravitation on the one hand and radiation and gas pressures on the other be disturbed, something is going to happen—and this is as far as we should go. Here is a possible explanation of a nova, and if it is the right one it implies that the nova phenomenon is a natural phase in the life of all stars. The sun has not reached that stage yet, so those who are interested in the end of the world have in store at least one way in which that event could be brought about, for in a few hours our friendly source of heat would become hundreds of thousands of times hotter, and the earth and all that is in it would return to the cosmic gas from which it presumably came. We do not really know what happens in these stars and even the most critical reader must agree that in the mechanism of pulsating stars and novae we have a genuinely unsolved mystery of the sky (3), (4), (5).

The Birth of the Planets

We have seen that for the last problem a variety of solutions have been put forward from time to time, one, maybe, in direct contradiction of another and none of them beyond criticism. The same applies here, and a brief account will be given of several interesting theories (6), beginning with the nebular hypothesis of Kant and Laplace, late eighteenth century. The theory starts from the assumption that there was a diffuse nebula, in dimension comparable with the whole solar system, and it was rotating. In course of time the nebula contracted under gravity; as it did so the velocity of rotation was increased, and this led to a flattening of the nebula until it had become a nucleus at the centre of a disk (rather like the frontispiece in appearance). The next stage was to suppose that as contraction continued rings of matter became detached and were left behind though still sharing the original rotation. These rings of matter then condensed to form the planets, and as they did so the ring casting process was repeated on a smaller scale and the satellites were born. Thus the final stage was a system of bodies all revolving in the same direction and in approximately the same plane. Highly inclined orbits and retrograde satellites were probably not known to Laplace at the time. This theory of steady evolution retained its popularity for 100 years, and then gave way to others based, not on evolution, but on some particular event. One serious objection to the nebular hypothesis is that the distribution of angular momentum is all wrong; the theory demands that most of the original momentum of the nebula (which obeys another conservation law) should be concentrated in the sun, whereas in fact 98 % of it is in the planets. We have also seen in Ch. IV that a small body like a satellite has insufficient gravity to retain an atmosphere. Thus a satellite could never have been produced from gravitating gas—if the moon cannot hold a gaseous atmosphere it could never have been wholly gaseous. There has recently been an attempt to overcome some of these objections.

The tidal theory, mainly associated with the name of Jeans (7), starts with a sun very much as it is now, and at some stage in its history a large star passed close by. The result of the encounter was that enormous tides were raised on the gaseous sun, and when the visitor was at its nearest point a long cigar-shaped filament of matter was pulled right out (Fig. 56A). This broke up into lumps that ultimately condensed into the planets, the biggest being in the middle where the cigar was thickest. The gravitational effect of the receding star would be to set up the motion of revolution around the sun, and in the plane of the star's motion relative to the sun, though in the early stages the orbits would be far from the near-circles that we now find. At this stage the primeval planets would pass close to the sun at perihelion, and the tidal disruption would be repeated to form the satellites. The large planets were still gaseous and acquired many satellites, all very much smaller than the parent body. The smaller planets were already approaching the liquid state, and either had no satellites at all, like Venus, or a small number tending to be larger in proportion to their parents. It is a rather pleasing theory, but suffers from the same weakness as the last—the inability to explain why the planets have so much angular momentum.

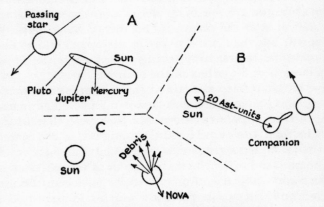

Fig. 56.   Theories of the birth of the planets

Other variants of the visiting star idea may be mentioned. One is that the planets were the result of a grazing collision. Another that the sun was one component of a binary system, its companion being at about the distance of Uranus. The effect of the visiting star in this case was to extract the tidal filament out of the companion (Fig. 56B), and this matter was captured by the sun to form the planets. Meanwhile the companion star was captured or otherwise removed by the visitor! In this theory the great distance and angular momentum of the planets is accounted for, but we are left wondering why they are now so evenly spread out instead of being bunched in the Neptune region.

The story told in Hoyle's broadcasts (2) also began with a binary star, but in this case the sun's companion developed into a super-nova. In this explosion there was a rocket effect: the main body of the companion was driven in one direction, away from the sun, and the debris the other (Fig. 56c). Some of the debris were captured by the sun and became the planets. This theory is not generally accepted, but then nor are any of the others either, so it is impossible so much as to suggest which is the *current* explanation of the origin of the solar system.

Nothing has been said about the minor constituents of our system, comets, meteors, minor planets. The matter can, of course, be airily dismissed by saying that whichever method you chose for the production of the planets there will be some fragments over. One difficulty would be to explain how such small accretions of matter could come about, and it is probably easier to accept the idea of the explosion of a larger body which had already condensed into something approaching solid form. With comets and meteors there is the added problem of whether they belong to the solar system at all, for the orbits of a few appear to be hyperbolic, and a hyperbola is an open curve from and to infinity. Some evidence has been put forward to suggest that when the orbit we observe is an open one it is really a former closed one that has been disturbed by perturbation due to the planets, and that the comet, although it may leave our system, did at least originate in it. Bearing in mind that comets can 'wear out', e.g. Biela's comet, page 138, there must be a pretty extensive cloud of potential comets in our neighbourhood to maintain the supply of new ones observed year by year. This unsolved problem of the origin of comets is one upon which work is being done at the present time (8), (9).

The Lunar Craters

So many readers will themselves have seen these features that, though the problem of their origin has not the fundamental importance of the foregoing, some space should be devoted to it. There are two main approaches, one assuming that the cause was internal and the other external.

The name 'crater', used on account of appearance, certainly suggests volcanic origin, and there are volcanic districts in the world which faintly resemble the lunar surface, though on a very much smaller scale. Our crater is the actual opening through which the eruption proceeds; it is difficult to imagine one 60 miles across! An old theory, proposed many years ago and no longer tenable, is that early in the moon's history there were eruptions of explosive violence; the expelled matter was thrown high above the surface and afterwards fell into a ring 20 or more miles from the point of explosion. Later there occurred in some cases a minor eruption that built a central mountain. Even bearing in mind that the force of gravity on the moon is much less than here, and that the average density of the material may be a little lower, it is difficult to see so much material being thrown so far, and one wonders why there are no intermediate deposits between the ring and the central peak.

Another form of volcanic action is to suppose that the crater floor was caused by a mighty outflow of molten lava which levelled everything in its path. Where the flow terminated there was a natural boundary of undestroyed hills; the central mountain, if any, marks the site of the outflow. Yet another is that in the process of cooling there was something akin to bubbles, and when these burst they left crater-like formations. Some years ago there appeared in *Discovery* (10) a photograph showing under the microscope the surface of welded steel. This showed precisely the effect described—the surface was dotted with lunar-like pits. A variant of this is that the bubbles were dome-like intrusions of lava, and in due time the crown collapsed into the molten mass, leaving the rough edge as the basis of the familiar ring mountain.

From time to time a meteorite strikes the earth's surface and makes a crater, as described in Ch. V. May not the moon, unprotected by atmosphere, have in the past been bombarded with meteorites? Again the size is a difficulty, and it seems likely that the earth would have shared to some extent in the bombardment. There is a famous meteor crater in Arizona; this is nearly a mile in diameter and 575 feet deep. Iron meteorites have been found in its neighbourhood. The age of the crater, on geological grounds, cannot exceed a few thousand years; the earth would then be very much the same as now, for in astronomical terms this is only yesterday. Until recently this was the largest known meteor crater, but recently the Ungava object in Northern Canada has been identified as such. This is a circular frozen lake 850 feet deep and two miles in diameter, the rim rising to a maximum of 500 feet above the water. Meteoric iron has been detected magnetically but not actually picked up (11). But how small are these compared with Tycho and Copernicus!

In support of the meteoric theory Baldwin carried out an investigation on the ratio of depth to diameter for craters of all kinds, the late war having provided ample material for the purpose. He included shell and bomb craters of various sizes and also that due to an industrial explosion. When these results were suitably plotted on a graph it was found that not only these, but also terrestrial meteor pits and the lunar craters, all lay on the same line. This is regarded as evidence that they are all due to the same cause, explosion, and what but meteorites could cause such explosions? (12)

Long before this, back in 1918, experiments were made on a small scale to see what kind of pits were made by falling objects. This was done by dropping cement powder on to a thin layer of the same substance, and then photographing the result, which did in fact resemble the lunar craters in appearance and relative dimensions. It seemed that the presence or otherwise of the central mountain depended upon the thickness of the soft layer in which the impact took place.

Against this evidence is the fact that we never see meteor impacts on the moon, and one big enough to produce a visible crater would certainly cause a flash. This may be explained by supposing that the moon does retain some atmosphere, for such a shield, though too tenuous to detect from here, would disintegrate most meteorites before they reached the surface. Another ingenious suggestion is that the impacts were not meteoric at all, but that the moon was once a binary planet. The smaller component came within Roche's limit and broke up, causing the moon to be bombarded with the bits. The moon would then, since the event, have been captured by the earth. Opinions are still very divided about the origin of the wonderful lunar surface.

Life in Other Worlds

The title of this section is also the title of a whole book (13), so it is obvious that only a brief treatment of the subject can be given here. What is life? How did life begin? These are questions for the biologists. By the former the average man is probably thinking of some animal form capable of consciousness; in answer to the latter let us just assume that life would occur wherever and whenever conditions are favourable, for that seems to be Nature's way of doing things. The problem at the moment, then, resolves itself into seeking conditions approximating to those existing upon the earth.

Reference to Chapters IV and V should convince the reader that of the members of the solar system only Mars and Venus can be seriously considered as possible abodes of life. Their temperatures are different, Mars being a cold planet and Venus a hot one, though this factor alone need not debar the existence of life. There would be some areas on each to which terrestrial life could adapt itself, for the adaptability of the living creature, though the process of natural selection, is one of the marvels of creation. Their atmospheres present more difficulty. Oxygen is the key to life as we know it; oxidation is the source of living energy, but these two planets have little or none of this apparently essential element. Plant life absorbs carbon dioxide, which does occur on Venus, and releases free oxygen, so unless the lower atmosphere of this planet has a different composition from the upper it would seem that there is no plant life, and presumably no animal life either. This leaves Mars, where we can see something that might be vegetation. The possibility of conscious beings on this planet cannot be ruled out, though there is no positive evidence and we cannot tell what form it would take. In his famous story *War of the Worlds* Wells gave them the form of the octopus and his fancy is just as good as any other. In the sun's planetary system, then, there are three possible abodes of life: two probable, and one definite—our own.

What about other planetary systems? This question is bound up with the theories of their formation. If you accept an evolutionary one, like the untenable nebular hypothesis, planets might happen to any star, and one or more of these planets might provide conditions favourable to life. Under these circumstances life would be quite commonplace in the universe. A cataclysmic theory makes the production of planets a chancy affair, and if, as in several of them, a close approach of two stars is a necessary condition, the chance is a very poor one. You know how empty space is, about the same—quoting Jeans —as three wasps in the whole of Europe; what chance is there of a meeting between these wasps? If this is the creation theory that you accept, then you accept with it the rarity of life. The nova theory gives rather more possibilities, even though to us a nova is an occasion of interest, for astronomical time is long. If there be one super-nova per century, if one in three happens to be a component of a binary, if in one case in ten the companion captures the debris, if in one in hundred of these new planets life occurs—the prospect sounds rather poor, but there will still be a lot of 'live births' in fifty thousand million years! Not all the abodes of life would be functioning at the same time, and maybe at the present time we are still the only one. Eddington put the situation very soundly when he pointed out that, whatever theory you adopt, what has happened once may happen again. There may have been creatures like us in the past, and there may be again in the future, but the chances are that at the moment man is unique.

The answer to our problem is, therefore, that there is no direct evidence for the existence of life anywhere but on earth. There are certain very tentative possibilities;

you have the facts before you and in this matter your guess is as good as mine.

The Expanding Universe

It was mentioned in the last chapter that the extra-galactic nebulae showed red shifts in their spectra, which, on the usual interpretation as radial velocities, indicate that they are receding from us at speeds proportional to their distances. There are three ways of accounting for this observation.

First, let us take it at its face value; all our neighbours really are running away from us at fantastic and ever increasing speeds, as if we were right at the very heart of a colossal explosion. But is it quite like that? Imagine a map drawn upon a sheet of rubber; it must be a good piece of rubber with uniform elasticity all over. Now let it be stretched so that its length and breadth are doubled in a time of one second. Then any point on that map will be twice as far from any other point as it was before. Take a point O as a definite reference. The point A, formerly one inch away, is now two inches, whereas B, formerly six inches, is now 12. To a flea at O, A has receded with a velocity of one inch per second, and B, which was six times as far off, with a velocity of six inches per second. So to any fleas that may be situated on that map every other flea will appear to be receding with a velocity proportional to his distance, but we, outside the map, can see what is really happening. Note that it is only the distances, not the fleas, that are increasing. This is the first explanation of the red shift; the nebulae are not running away from mankind in particular, but the space containing them and us is expanding.

The second explanation is that the observed velocities

are the result of a random distribution of motions which have been going on for a long time. Consider a lot of boys not very far from a pole in the middle of a large field. Let them all start running or walking in any direction they like, provided it is a straight line. Some will at first approach the pole; others will go directly away from it; yet others will be going towards the edge of the field with little reference to the pole. Soon after the movement begins there will be some congestion in the vicinity of the pole, but after a while every boy will be increasing his distance from it, and those who run fastest will be the farthest away. Thus a random distribution of velocities a long time ago could have become an apparently systematic one now. In a way this is more satisfactory than the last. The expanding universe is a frightening thought; but why worry?—what we see is quite natural and simply must happen if the galaxies have any uniform motion whatever!

The third explanation is not an explanation at all: it is a way out. It attributes the red shift to some cause not yet explained, a cause due, not to velocity at all, but to some kind of energy loss to which light is subject over a very long journey. There is no evidence for this loss, but when a machine produces some inexplicable result it is is so comforting to be able to say 'there is something wrong with the works'. Mind, this may in the end prove to be the right approach, and it is offered here on equal terms with the other two. The choice is the reader's.

Perhaps an author may be pardoned, in his last chapter, for not being impartial, but there is some solid evidence in favour of No. 1, and from an entirely different quarter. Relativity, in its widest sense, is a new mathematical outlook, associated with the name of Einstein and since 1905 developed by him and other workers. Einstein himself added a corner stone to this edifice as recently as 1950. When this new mathematics is applied to natural phenomena it is found to explain them more accurately than the old, and we have already noted one example of it in the motion of Mercury. One of the early workers, De Sitter, on applying the new principle to the universe as a whole, came to the conclusion that it should be expanding, and was therefore in a position to say 'I told you so' when the recession of the nebulae was subsequently discovered. At that time Einsten himself had worked out a stationary system, but it was also unstable and therefore liable to expand (or contract) if its perfect balance were to be disturbed. Bearing in mind the early parts of this chapter it is not surprising that the Einstein equilibrium has been disturbed (14), (15). Interesting though this prediction may be it is not conclusive, and the problem of whether the universe is expanding or not is still a very open one.

Let us assume for the present that the expansion is real and tackle the question 'how big is the universe?'. So far every larger telescope has revealed more of space than its predecessor. In the last chapter it was mentioned that the Palomar telescope is expected to double the distance of 500 million light years already explored. How much more is there to see? Taking the velocity of a nebula to be 100 miles per second for each million light years of its distance, then if the distance were 1860 million light years it would be travelling as fast as light. Then, of course, we could never see it at all, for the distance between us and the nebula would be increasing at the same rate as the light was crossing it. This would give the limit of size of *observable* space at about 2×10^9 light

years. Is there any more? Can we say that if the further
space cannot be detected it does not exist? Hardly, but
another argument can be quoted for what it is worth. One
of the earlier conclusions from relativity (but now ques-
tioned) is that nothing can travel faster than light: anything beyond 2×10^9 light years must travel faster than
light; therefore there is nothing beyond 2×10^9. A bit
thin perhaps but there it is. It is hard to believe that
space is infinite, that it just goes on for ever and ever, but
if we say that it stops we are faced with an even tougher
problem: what is over the boundary. Another dip into
relativity may give an escape from this dilemma, though
not all astronomers wish to escape or even admit the
existence of the dilemma.

At this point the fourth dimension turns up, and this
word 'dimension' has caused trouble to non-specialists for
over 20 years. Positions in ordinary conventional space
can be specified in terms of three numbers or coordinates,
which in an ordinary room could conveniently be length,
breadth and height. This is the familiar three-dimensional
space, and the ordinary space problems in mathematics
can be set out as equations involving three variables, say
x, y and z. Exercises of this kind are done by university
students under the title of 'coordinate geometry (or ana-
lytical geometry) of three dimensions', thus distinguishing
it from the more familiar graph drawing in two dimensions
that we all of us did at school. When the new mathematics, or relativity, is applied, the operator finds that he
needs a minimum of four variables, and by analogy with
the foregoing would speak of his 'four-dimensional equations'. Thus 'four dimensions' in astronomy is concerned
with what the mathematics, not the space itself, looks like,
for 'looking' is confined to three. If a picture of a flat

(two-dimensional) object be made, it can be a perfect representation of it, for the picture is itself two dimensional. If the object is a solid, with depth to it, the picture cannot be a perfect reproduction; it is a two-dimensional view of a three-dimensional object. As, however, we are accustomed to three-dimensions, having eyes and hands with which to perceive three, we can usually infer what the actual object is like, and possibly with some modelling material make a tolerably good copy of it. Now when we look around us we are perceiving a three-dimensional view of a space which mathematics tells us is really four, but here we must take his word for it. Don't try to picture it—it can't be done. If the mathematician or philosopher wants to use four, five, six or any other number of variables in his work, don't worry; leave them as they are, quantities, some of which are individually familiar—such as length, breadth, height, and the usual fourth, time—and some are not (16).

Confine your attention for a moment to one dimension; say parallel to the top edge of the page: the only lines you can draw must necessarily be straight. Now allow yourself two dimensions, the whole surface of the paper, and your pencil lines can be curved ones—an impossibility before. Draw straight lines on the paper and allow yourself a third dimension, the one you use when you turn over: the paper can bend, so that your lines that were straight in two dimensions may be curved in three. It is not really necessary to draw these things at all, for they can be represented by equations, and the equations will show whether the lines or planes are curved. A plane in two dimensions can be curved if a third is available, and the mathematics can show it. Space in three dimensions can be curved if a fourth is available, and Einstein's mathematics showed that it was curved in the vicinity of a massive body. If space becomes curved so do straight lines in that space, like the straight lines on the bent paper, and this is something capable of an experimental test. At the total eclipse of 1919 photographs were taken to show the stars close to the eclipsed sun. Light travels in straight lines, but those particular light rays had to pass close to the massive sun, where space was said to be curved. Thus the rays should be bent a little and star positions be slightly different from those in photographs taken when the sun was not in that direction. They were, and by just about as much as Einstein expected. Thus space not only can be curved, it sometimes demonstrably is, though it must be admitted that with the lapse of time the enthusiasm for this demonstration has begun to wane. By applying relativity mathematics to the universe it can be shown that, besides local curvatures like the above, there is a general one. Space curves back upon itself and joins up, like the two-dimensional surface of a globe joins up. If this theory of closed space be accepted—it is not universally so by any means—it means that there is no embarrassing boundary. Space is finite but boundless; there is a definite amount to wander in but no wall—the wanderer would just, in time, get back to where he started. If we believe that the expansion is real, then our boundless playground is for ever getting larger. In the last few pages we have been dangerously near a boundary of another sort—that between astronomy and philosophy, one which the present writer is certainly not qualified to cross (17), (18). The allotted number of pages for this book is rapidly running out, and there is one more problem arising out of the expanding universe.

In the cosmology of 20 or 30 years ago the sequence of

P

events was something like this: the primeval gas separated into clumps, afterwards to become galaxies; this condensation was repeated on a smaller scale, to form stars; some stars divided into binary systems, while at least one acquired planets. All this would take a very long time to come about, time measured in millions of millions of years, say 10^{12} for a star and 10^{14} for a galaxy. As to the future, the universe was running down and would die when the energy, now concentrated in stars, had become uniformly dissipated through radiation into space. The time estimates were based on criteria such as the period required for observed stellar motions to have reached their present state, or for a binary star newly formed by fission to have acquired its present orbit.

Although the long time scale still has some adherents the expansion of the universe has shaken it to its foundations, for in geological time since the earth's crust was formed the external galaxies have at least doubled their distance. At no very distant past all must have been in a state of congestion, and if this was the moment of creation, then the stars and nebulae cannot be vastly older than the earth itself. The age of the earth (p. 114) gives us a reasonably certain minimum, and the maximum according to current thought may be as much as five times that. Thus, on the short time scale the date since the creation lies between two and ten thousand million. What of the future? What is our expectation of life? Some kind of local answer might be attempted, for knowing (do we?) the mechanism of the sun's generation of energy it is possible to estimate how long it would last. An estimate of this kind, based on hydrogen content, comes to 50,000 million years, of which by far the greater portion is yet to come. Assuming that other stars will behave in a comparable manner, and remembering that some stars are younger than ours, this would give some idea of the date for the 'running down' to be complete. In very much less than this all the visible galaxies will have acquired the velocity of light, which some authorities maintain cannot be exceeded; what happens then, apart from their disappearance from our night sky? This is all very difficult and perhaps it is easier not to try to put a limit on time. Hoyle adopts the view (2) that it is infinite in both directions, and that as old galaxies expand out the range of vision, so new ones develop to take their place. Our own little world will have its end in due course, but the great universe, in which there are or will be other little worlds like ours, will go on for ever and ever. Perhaps— or perhaps not—but at least it provides a hopeful thought of immortality with which to lay down this book.

REFERENCES

(1) See Davidson, *From Atoms to Stars*, 1946, where a summary of the various theories will be found.

(2) The broadcast talks have been published: F. Hoyle, *The Nature of the Universe*, 1950.

(3) For earlier views on stellar energy and evolution see J. H. Jeans, *The Universe Around Us*, 1st ed. 1929.

(4) See also G. Gamov, *The Birth and Death of the Sun*.

(5) A students' book on modern work is M. Johnson, *Astronomy of Stellar Energy and Decay*, 1950.

(6) See Reference (1), and also W. M. Smart, *The Origin of the Earth*, 1951.

(7) Described in his *Universe Around Us*.

(8) The topic was discussed by G. Merton in his Presidential Address, *Journal of the B.A.A.*, 62/11, 1951.

(9) See also O. Struve, 'The Origin of Comets', in *Sky and Telescope*, IX/82, 1950.

(10) C. G. James, 'The Problem of the Lunar Craters', *Discovery*, I/157, 1938.

(11) Photograph and short description of the Ungava crater appear in *Sky and Telescope*, XI/2, 1951. Account and map in *Observatory*, 71/122, 1951.

(12) R. B. Baldwin, *The Face of the Moon*, U.S.A. The graph has been reproduced in *Discovery*, X/271, 1949.

(13) H. Spencer Jones, *Life in Other Worlds*, revised 1952.

(14) For further reading A. S. Eddington, *The Expanding Universe*, 1933, can be recommended. Though no longer new it is a joy to read for anyone prepared to give a little concentration. Some thoughts on this topic also appear in Ref. (2).

(15) Also a lecture (since published): J. H. Jeans, *The Astronomical Horizon*, 1944.

(16) For life in four dimensions—coupled with cheerful reading—see G. Gamov, *Mr. Tomkins in Wonderland*, 1939.

(17) See the writings of Eddington and Jeans; at this point the most suitable is probably Jeans' *Mysterious Universe*, 1930.

(18) Also G. C. McVittie, 'The Cosmological Problem', *Science News* No. 21 (Penguin), 1951.

LIST OF OBSERVATIONAL AIDS

NUMEROUS books for general reading have already been noted; here are a few suggestions for the benefit of readers who wish to undertake some observations of their own.

CONSTELLATION GUIDES

Stars at a Glance, George Philip.
Philip's Planisphere, George Philip.

OBSERVATIONAL HANDBOOKS

For young people:
Observing the Heavens, Peter Hood, Oxford.
Guide to the Sky, E. A. Beet, Cambridge.

For older people:
Introducing Astronomy, J. B. Sidgwick, Faber.

STAR ATLAS, with lists of objects for the telescope

New Popular Star Atlas, Gall & Inglis.
Norton's Star Atlas and Reference Handbook, Gall & Inglis,
more comprehensive, with extensive notes.

THE CHOICE OF A TELESCOPE

See F. M. Holborn in *Journal of B.A.A.*, Jan. 1948.

PERIODICALS

The Times Astronomical Column; first weekday each month.
Monthly: *Sky and Telescope*; Harvard College Observatory,
Cambridge 38, Mass. U.S.A.
Eight per year: *Journal of the B.A.A.*, free to members.
Six per year, current astronomical thought and progress, not
primarily for observers: *The Observatory*, Royal Greenwich
Observatory, Herstmonceux Castle, Hailsham, Sussex.

ASSOCIATION OF OBSERVERS

The British Astronomical Association, 303 Bath Road, Hounslow
West, Middx, annual subscription 45/-.

Index

Main reference, where applicable, in heavy type; italics refer to illustrations